CLIL in English
Technology and the Society

CLILで学ぶ工学と社会

Shigeru Sasajima
Masayuki Takahashi
Yuko Uesugi
Kumiko Okazaki
Keisuke Tanino
Taichi Kawakami
Chiari Isami
Brian Shaw
Aleksandra Zaparucha

NAN'UN-DO

まえがき

学習者へ

本教科書は、CLIL (Content and Language Integrated Learning)（内容と言語を統合した学習）の考え方をもとにした英語の理解と実践を支援します。「英語を勉強する」という思い込みは少し脇に置いて、英語で「工学と社会」を思考しましょう。また、工学 (technology) という内容 (content) を、私たちの社会環境 (contexts) で、コミュニケーション (communication) として必要な英語（English）で理解し、英語を使って学ぶことを目的としています。

英語の単語をおぼえ、アメリカ人のように発音できるように練習し、正しい文法を学び、正確に使えるように読み・書きを中心に学習し、それと同じように聞き・話すためにテストを受け、資格を得る。そのような実際の英語の運用とは少しかけ離れた学習活動とは縁を切って、工学という分野で英語を通してどのような知識を得て、それをどのように使って、世界中の工学に携わる人と知識や技能を共有するかを、この教科書を通じて考えてください。そのためには、文化と文化の関係性の理解 (intercultural awareness) が必要です。

工学は知識だけでは意味がありません。社会と強くかかわっています。その社会は日本語だけの社会ではほぼ意味がないでしょう。英語は必須です。それも、世界中で使われる英語 (ELF: English as a Lingua Franca) のコミュニケーション力が必要です。工学に興味があり、工学の分野に進む人にとっては、それはそれほどむずかしいことではありません。そのために少しでも寄与できたら幸いです。

先生へ

大学工学部、高専、工業高校などを対象として編纂してありますが、あくまで教材です。担当の先生の裁量で工夫して扱ってください。Unit は順番に扱う必要はありません。学習者の興味を優先して、幅を広げてください。さらに、教科書をすべて学ぶ必要はありません。まずは学びを楽しむことです。テストや活動については補助教材をつけますが、適宜利用してください。

CLIL について

CLIL は決して特別な学習法でも学習指導でもありません。工学という内容を英語と日本語で理解し、英語でコミュニケーションしようとする活動を後押しすることを目的にしています。そのために、学習者自身が目標を持ち、ゴールを想定し、工学を英語で理解し、その知識を英語で活用できるようにプロセスとして CLIL を考えてください。実験や試作と同様に、失敗の積み重ねが成功への一歩です。CLIL は、そのための統合学習です。工学への興味があれば、英語は自然に身につきます。失敗を楽しみましょう。

著者一同

本教科書を活用する学習者の学び方について

扱っている内容は、工学の一般的な内容です。専門的には物足りないかもしれません。それぞれ自主的にインターネットなどで検索し自分の専門分野について深く学んでください。CLIL の大きな特徴は自律学習 (learner autonomy) です。与えられた知識や英語活動をただ学んでいるだけでは、CLIL の大きな特徴となっている次の「4 つの C(4Cs)」を生かすことできません。

内容 (Content) — 工学のおもしろさに気づく
思考 (Cognition) — 工学を英語と関連し工夫する
コミュニケーション (Communication) — 工学の話題を英語で伝え合う
文化 (Culture) — 工学と社会を英語と日本語でふりかえる

上記の CLIL の特徴を生かすには多様性と柔軟性がカギです。「学習はかくあるべき」はやめましょう。知識や技能を楽しむこと、英語はただの道具と割り切ること、自分にとって大切なことは何かが分かれば、CLIL は自然に理解できます。

上記のことを達成するために、各 Unit の構成は次のようになっています。

1. *CLIL attainment target*（学習目標）

2. *Introduction*（導入）
Practice 1 Listen and check your understanding（リスニング）
Practice 2 Read and check your understanding（リーディング）
Practice 3 Talk in pairs（英語で話す）

3. *Topic 1*（工学の話題 1）
Practice 4 (Reading question)（読むポイント）

4. *Text summarization*（要約のしかた）
Practice 5 Summary of Topic 1 Recite it（要約の暗唱）
Practice 6 Read and summary（要約する）

5. *Topic 2*（工学の話題 2）
Practice 7 (Discussion)（内容を英語で話し合う）

6. *Understanding key terms*（話題の重要語句）
Practice 8 (Discussion)（内容を英語で話し合う）

7. *Learning outcomes*（学習成果）
Self-assessment（自己評価）
Practice 9 A summary of learning（学習のまとめ）

教科書内容は、できる限り英語で工学を学ぶ人に役立つように工夫しました。しかし、物足りないところがあると思います。興味のあることは、ぜひ自分なりに深く追求してください。CLIL はそれを応援します。

Unit 1 7

Artificial intelligence (AI): present and future

Unit 2 13

3D printing: technology that makes our life more comfortable

Unit 3 19

Power electronics supporting our life

Technology column 1 25

A history of engineering

Unit 4 27

Eco-housing for a better life

Unit 5 33

Flow and the energy: fluid dynamics is useful in our life

Unit 6 39

Electric vehicles (EVs): technology for assisting us

Technology column 2 45

Saving energy

Unit 7 47

Rescue robots as substitutes in danger

Unit 8 53

Nanotechnology to change our life

Unit 9 59

The hydrogen fuel cell train

Technology column 3 65

Some issues of IoT

Unit 10 67

Protein: research expands to outer space

Unit 11 73

Shifting to renewable energy

Unit 12 79

Nature learning: engineers look to the natural world

Technology column 4 85

Withdrawing water from the air

CLIL in English
Technology and the Society

by

Shigeru Sasajima
Masayuki Takahashi
Yuko Uesugi
Kumiko Okazaki
Keisuke Tanino
Taichi Kawakami
Chiari Isami
Brian Shaw
Aleksandra Zaparucha

Download Audio

音声ファイル 無料 DL のご案内

このテキストの音声を無料で視聴（ストリーミング）・ダウンロードできます。自習用音声としてご活用ください。
以下のサイトにアクセスしてテキスト番号で検索してください。

https://nanun-do.com　テキスト番号［ **512179** ］

※ 無線 LAN（WiFi）に接続してのご利用を推奨いたします。

※ 音声ダウンロードは Zip ファイルでの提供になります。
お使いの機器によっては別途ソフトウェア（アプリケーション）の導入が必要となります。

CLIL in English—Technology and the Society 音声ダウンロードページは左記の QR コードからもご利用になれます。

Read by

Emma Howard
Shizuka Anderson
Kyle Card
Ryan Drees

Unit 1

Artificial intelligence (AI): present and future

AI の現在と未来

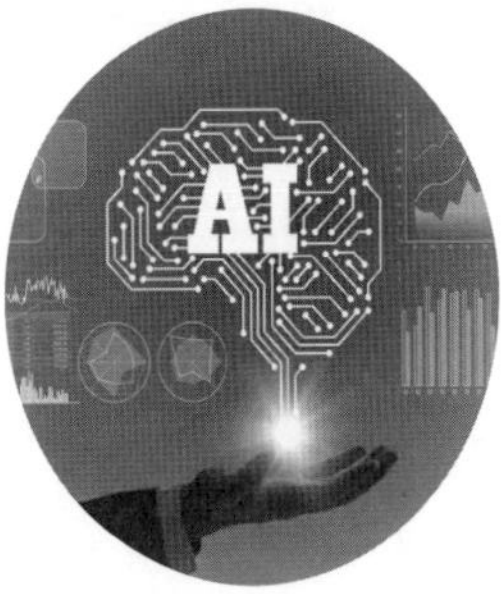

1. *CLIL attainment target*　この課の学習目標を確認しよう

1. I can listen to and read **what artificial intelligence (AI) is.**	聞く・読む技能
2. I can speak and write about **how AI is used in our daily life.**	話す・書く技能
3. I can understand **the ideas and problems about AI.**	関連の内容の理解

2. *Introduction*　*What is AI?*　AI とは何か？

Practice 1 **Listen and check your understanding**　聞き取ってみよう　02

1) Which computer language is Takashi going to study?

a) Java　　b) Python　　c) C#

2) How did Takashi get to know about AI research?

a) He read books.　　b) He googled it.　　c) He asked AI.

Practice 2 **Read and check your understanding**　情報を理解しよう　03

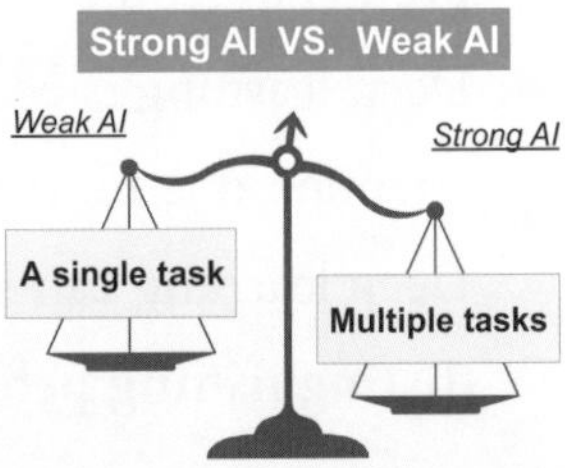

There are two types of AI – weak AI and strong AI. Weak AI refers to systems that can solve a limited range of problems by performing a pre-defined set of functions. Virtual personal assistants, such as Apple's Siri and Amazon's Alexa, are examples of weak AI. Strong AI refers to systems that can think and perform complex tasks on their own, similar to human beings. Such systems can "think for themselves" and thus, can find **solutions**《解決》 to unfamiliar tasks without human **intervention**《介入》. Although strong AI sometimes appears in science fiction movies, it currently remains a theoretical concept. As research and development continues to advance, strong AI may eventually emerge.

Practice 3 **Talk in pairs**　内容を確認して、英語でおしゃべりしよう

What is the difference between weak AI and strong AI? Where is AI used around you?

e.g.　A: Do you know the difference between weak AI and strong AI?

B: Yes. It's easy. The systems are different. Do you know where AI is used?

A: Yes. AI is used in lots of places.

3. *Topic 1　AI as a savior for the future*　AIは救世主　04

Practice 4　**Do you think AI can be a savior for our future life?**　AIは救世主ですか

1. AI can be a savior for the future. Some people may think that the development of AI is a big threat to humans. They worry about AI's potential to **take over**《引き継ぐ》 jobs currently performed by human workers. However, such a view may be too pessimistic, since it fails to see the positive impacts that AI will have on future society.

2. A declining **birthrate**《出生率》 and an **aging**《老齢》 population may result in worker shortages in the future, especially in Japan. AI can help **compensate for**《補う》 a shortage of workers by **automatically operating machinery and equipment**《自動で機械や道具を操作すること》.
3. Human beings and AI should create a **symbiotic relationship**《共生関係》. AI should not be viewed as a threat to human societies. **On the contrary**《他方》, AI should be accepted for its potential to solve social problems and prolong human life through improved health and **medical care**《医療》.
4. It is important to know how to use AI, machine learning, and deep learning. AI also includes machine learning and deep learning. These two ways of learning are part of AI.
5. Machine learning refers to efforts to teach machines or computers to learn the way human beings do. It uses computer algorithms and statistical models to analyze data and **predict**《予測する》 **outcomes**《結果》.
6. Deep learning is considered as part of machine learning. Moreover, it is gaining much attention due to its **supremacy**《卓越》 in terms of accuracy when it is trained with huge data. Deep learning can be used for many tasks such as understanding text documents and **distinguishing**《区別する》 people. Also, it is utilized in driverless cars and **speech recognition**《発話認識》 systems.
7. It is necessary to do more research on AI for the benefit of society. Since AI aspires to endow machines with abilities that replicate or exceed those of humans, research that helps us better understand how humans perform complex tasks can greatly aid the development of AI.

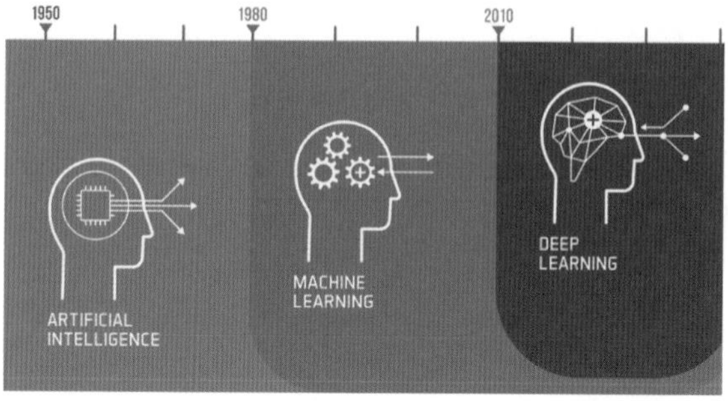

4. *Text summarization How to make a summary* 必要な情報のまとめ方

Practice 5 Summary of Topic 1 Recite it Topic 1（前ページ）のまとめ 暗唱しよう

1. AI can be a savior for the future.
2. A declining birthrate and an aging population may result in worker shortages.
3. Humans and AI should create a symbiotic relationship.
4. It is important to know how to use AI, machine learning, and deep learning.
5. Machine learning teaches machines or computers to learn the way human beings do.
6. Deep learning can be considered as part of machine learning.
7. It is necessary to do a lot more research on AI for the benefit of society.

Practice 6 Read and summarize 読んで内容を把握してサマリーを作成しよう 05

Alan Turing was a British **mathematician**《数学者》 and a founding father of the theory and development of AI. He invented the Turing test to determine if a machine could exhibit intelligent behavior equivalent to, or indistinguishable from, that of a human being. The test is designed to assess whether a machine can think or not.

The IBM supercomputer, Deep Blue, captured the world's imagination in 1997 when it defeated Garry Kasparov, the world's greatest chess champion at that time. The six-game match lasted several days, and Deep Blue had two wins, one defeat, and three draws.

An Expert System is a type of AI system designed to display and imitate aspects of **rational behavior**《合理的行動》. Expert Systems are widely used in commercial and industrial settings, such as medicine, finance, **manufacturing**《製造業》, sales, and video games.

Meta (or Facebook) and Twitter are two big companies that use AI to send users the right message at the right time. For example, Facebook has a function to introduce users who may somehow be connected.

In 1999, Sony released its first version of AIBO – a pet robot that people could play with. AIBO could express emotions and identify its owner. It was one of the first AI robots.

Complete the summary 適切な語を入れてサマリーを完成しよう

Alan Turing was a (   ) father of the theory and development of (   ). The IBM supercomputer, **Deep Blue**, (   ) the world's imagination in 1997. **An Expert System** is designed to display and imitate aspects of (   ) behavior. **Meta (or Facebook)** and **Twitter** are two big companies that use AI to send users the right (   ) at the right (   ). In 1999, (   ) released its first version of **AIBO**.

Research **What are you interested in when reading this passage? Choose one and do research.**

5. *Topic 2 The singularity in AI* AIのシンギュラリティ（特異点）

06

Practice 7 **The singularity in AI is a point at which AI can learn and improve itself faster than humans. Do you think it is possible? Discuss whether or not AI will surpass human intelligence.** AIは人間の知性を超えますか？

AI will bring about the singularity. Have you ever heard of the term 'singularity'? According to Dictionary.com, singularity is defined as 'the state, fact, or quality of being singular.'

The singularity in AI refers to the technological singularity, which means a point in the future when AI **surpasses**《越える》 human intelligence. The singularity is expected to come around 2045.

Although human beings have developed AI, it may evolve by itself in the future. If AI continues to develop rapidly, it may be able to **strengthen itself**《強くなる》. Many scientists expect much of human work to be replaced by AI over time.

Even now, AI can find and identify diseases that human doctors can't see using X-ray images. AI has also been able to defeat highly skilled players of board games, such as chess and shogi. As the processing capacities of supercomputers continue to improve, so do the capabilities of AI.

Besides weak AI and strong AI, there is also super AI which represents a level of cognitive capability that surpasses human **intelligence**《知性》 and ability. Although weak AI is currently available and strong AI is being developed, super AI now only exists in **the world of science fiction**《SFの世界》.

Some scientists believe that humans can probably create strong AI, or Artificial General Intelligence (AGI), as some researchers call it. Once that is achieved, the singularity may soon occur. So, a future in which super AI exists may be approaching much faster than we expect.

SINGULARITY TIME LINE

Rise in human intelligence could be driven by AI in the future

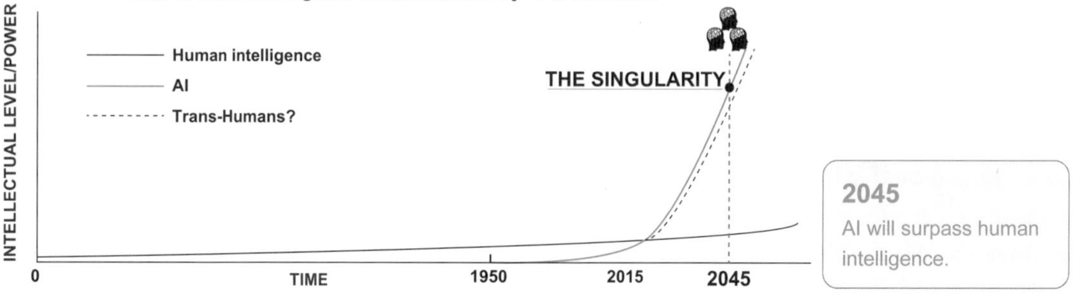

6. *Understanding AI Key terms* AIを考えるのに必要な用語

Practice 8 **Discuss the key terms on AI: AI, machine learning, deep learning and singularity**

AI

AI refers to computer systems with the **potential**《可能性》 to **adapt to**《適応する》 a variety of environments and situations and perform tasks that normally require human intelligence. For instance, many cars nowadays contain driver assistance systems, such as **blind-spot monitoring**《死角チェック》, **cross-traffic detectors**《交差交通検出》, emergency braking, and driver-assist steering. These are basic examples of AI.

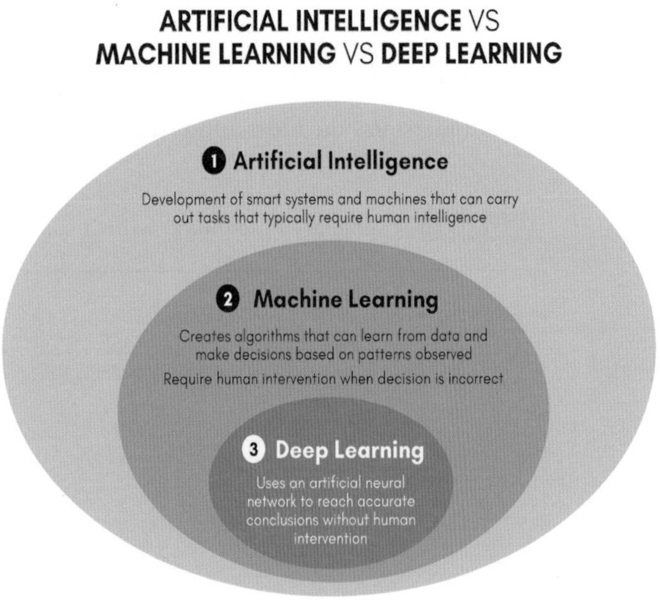

www.scs.org.sg/

Machine learning

Machine learning refers to algorithms and statistical models that enable computers to perform specific tasks, without explicit instructions. The machine "decides" what to do by analyzing data, discovering patterns, and making predictions. For example, machine learning can be used in conjunction with image processing systems to enable **autonomous vehicles**《自律運転自動車》 to detect roadway conditions and steer appropriately. This technology is not new. As computer hardware develops and computers are able to process larger and larger volumes of data, machine learning speeds up. Also, as AI research produces more efficient learning models, the speed and efficiency of machine learning systems will continue to improve.

Deep learning

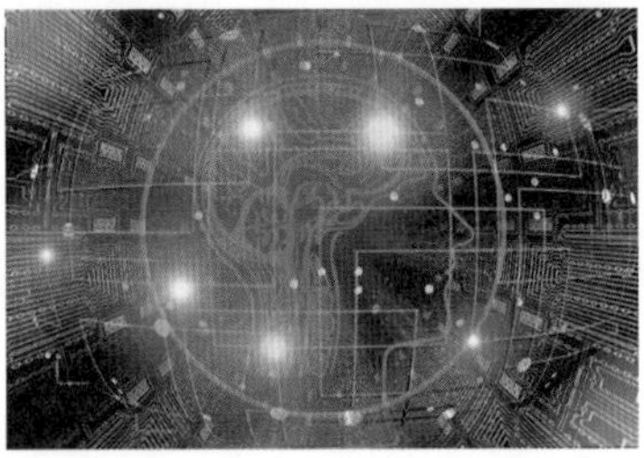

Deep learning is part of a family of machine learning methods that utilize algorithms **inspired**《触発された》 by **artificial neural networks**《人工神経》. These methods are intended to train AI to think and learn as humans do. While **endowing**《授ける》 machines with such abilities has been a challenge, it is now more possible than ever due to deep learning tools and technology.

7. *Learning outcomes* *What have you learned?* 学んだことの整理

Self-assessment 自己評価をしよう

I can listen to and read **what AI is**.	0---30---50---70---100%
I can speak and write about **how AI is used in our daily life**.	0---30---50---70---100%
I can understand **the ideas and problems about AI**.	0---30---50---70---100%

Practice 9 **A summary of learning: write a summary of what you have learned in this unit.**

Key terms

Key sentences

Key facts

Your understanding

Your thoughts

Unit 2

3D printing: technology that makes our life more comfortable

3Dプリンタ：生活を快適にしてくれる技術

1. *CLIL attainment target*　この課の学習目標を確認しよう

1. I can listen to and read **what 3D printing is.** 聞く・読む技能
2. I can speak and write about **how 3D printing works.** 話す・書く技能
3. I can understand **the ideas and problems about 3D printing.** 関連の内容の理解

2. *Introduction*　*What is 3D printing?*　3D printingとは何か？

Practice 1 **Listen and check your understanding**　聞き取ってみよう　07

1) Which is necessary to make something with a 3D printer?

a) plastic　　b) a model　　c) design data

2) What did the **vet**《獣医》 make for an injured dog?

a) a real bone　　b) a 3D printed bone　　c) injured bone

Practice 2 **Read and check your understanding**　情報を理解しよう　08

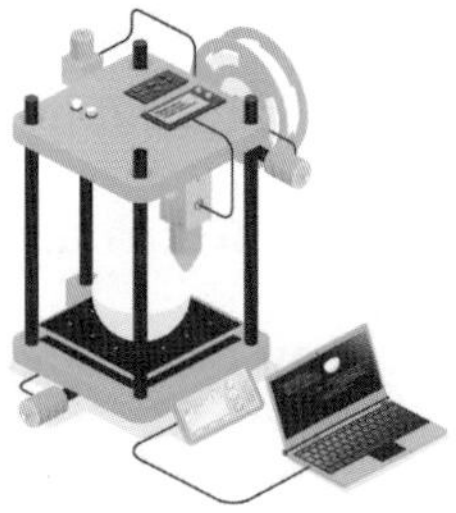

3D printing is a process of creating **three-dimensional**《3次元の》 objects from computer-aided design (CAD) models by **layering**《層状物質》 **materials**, such as **polymer filament**《ポリマーフィラメント》 or **metal powder**《金属粉》, until objects are made. The process requires the use of a 3D printer that builds objects based upon data contained in the CAD models. Due to its flexibility and low cost, 3D printing is used in various fields, such as **manufacturing**《製造業》, **architecture**《建築》, and **medicine**《医療》, to build models and **prototypes**《試作品》. Despite its many advantages, some people are worried about the potential for this powerful technology to be misused.

Practice 3 **Talk in pairs**　内容を確認して、英語でおしゃべりしよう

Are you interested in 3D printing? Have you seen 3D printed things before?

e.g.　A: Do you want to use 3D printers?

B: Yes, I'd love to. It's very fun to make what I want to use.

A: Sounds nice, but I'm afraid about the cost

3. *Topic 1　The creation process of 3D printing*　3Dプリントの作成プロセス 09

Practice 4 **What type of objects do you want to make with a 3D printer? Why?**
3Dプリンターで何を造りたいですか

1. 3D printing or **additive manufacturing**《積層造形》 is a method of creating 3D objects by **stacking**《積み重ねる》 materials in layers. There are various techniques and materials used in 3D printing.

2. A 3D printer can be used to make a **solid**《固体》 or **hollow**《中空》 object. The printer can create an object from various materials, such as polymer, metal, ceramic, and wax.

3. You can create almost anything with a 3D printer if you have its design data. Just as a 2D printer can be used to print any text or image onto a sheet of paper, a 3D printer can be used to 'print' almost any 3D object if the design data is available.

4. Three steps are needed to create objects with a 3D printer: designing, slicing, and printing. First, the object must be designed on a computer using CAD software. Second, the design must be divided **horizontally**《水平に》 into 'slices.' This step can be done with software called a 'slicer.' Finally, the sliced data is sent to a 3D printer, which then 'prints' the object by stacking softened materials in horizontal layers. This results in a 3D object that matches the design data shown in the original CAD model.

5. There are several types of 3D printers: e.g. **Fused Deposition Modeling (FDM)**《熱溶解積層法》, **Stereolithography (SLA)**《ステレオリソグラフィー(光造形の一つ)》, **Digital Light Processing (DLP)**《デジタル光造形》, **Selective Laser Sintering (SLS)**《選択的レーザ焼結》, **Selective Laser Melting (SLM)**《選択的レーザ溶融法》, **Laminated Object Manufacturing (LOM)**《薄膜積層法》, and **Electron Beam Melting (EBM)**《電子ビーム溶解法》.

4. *Text summarization How to make a summary* 必要な情報のまとめ方

Practice 5 **Summary of Topic 1 Recite it** Topic 1（前ページ）のまとめ 暗唱しよう

1. 3D printing or additive manufacturing is a method of creating 3D objects.
2. A 3D printer can be used to make a solid or hollow object.
3. You can create almost anything with a 3D printer if you have its design data.
4. Three steps are needed to create objects with a 3D printer: designing, slicing, and printing.
5. There are several types of 3D printers.

Practice 6 **Read and summarize** 読んで内容を把握してサマリーを作成しよう 10

3D printing can be used to create some useful things, such as **prosthetics**《補綴：義足など》, artificial **organs**《臓器》, medical **equipment**《器具》, and **automobile**《自動車》 parts.

The production of prosthetics is one of the most **remarkable**《顕著な》 ways in which 3D printers can be used to benefit people's lives. Although prosthetics are expensive to produce using **conventional means**《従来の方法》, it is possible to create them using 3D printers at a greatly reduced cost.

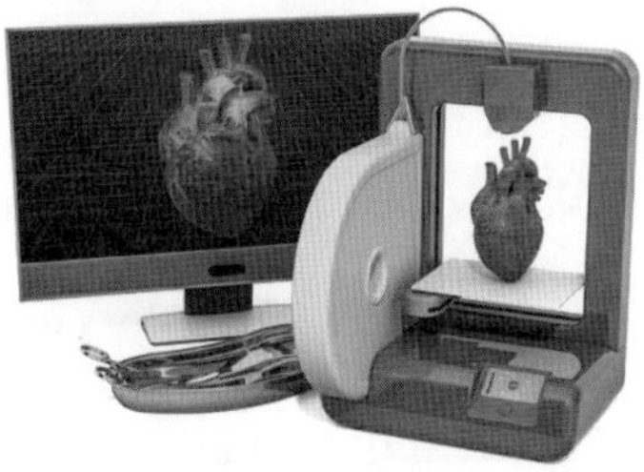

3D printing can also be used to make new organs for patients using their own cells. In the future, patients who require **replacement organs**《代わりの臓器》 will be able to have new organs created using their own cells. They will avoid the risks associated with **organ donation**《臓器提供》. The process, known as 3D **bioprinting**《バイオプリンティング》, enables living **cell tissues**《細胞組織》 to be joined in layers in a way similar to the printing of 3D objects in plastic.

3D printed automobile parts can be lighter than conventional parts. The **reduction**《減少》 in weight results in increased **fuel efficiency**《燃焼効率》 and more eco-friendly vehicles. After Volkswagen redesigned its **A-pillar**《車の前窓の柱》 window support with 3D printing, the new part weighed 74% less than the original one.

Complete the summary 適切な語を入れてサマリーを完成しよう

3D printing can be used to create some (　　　) things. The production of (　　　) is one of the most remarkable ways in which 3D (　　　) can be used to benefit people's lives. 3D printing can also be used to make new (　　　) for patients using their own cells. 3D printed (　　　) parts can be lighter than conventional parts.

Research **What are you interested in when reading this passage? Choose one and do research.**

5. *Topic 2 The Development of 3D printing* 3Dプリンターの開発 11

Practice 7 **How is 3D printing used around you?**

3Dプリンタはあなたの周りではどのように使われていますか？

3D printing **originated**《始まる》 in Japan. In 1980, a Japanese engineering researcher in Nagoya invented a stereolithography (SLA) method, which is an additive manufacturing process using a laser. At first, he wanted to obtain a **patent**《特許》, but gave it up when he realized no one was interested in it.

In the late 1980s, an American engineer obtained patents for additive manufacturing and called the method 3D printing. He founded a company and produced 3D printers.

In those days, 3D printers were very expensive, but after the patents **expired**《期限が切れた》 in 2009, many companies began to develop and sell 3D printers. As a result, 3D printers became widely available for use by individuals as well as small companies.

The **function**《機能》 and **performance**《性能》 of 3D printers have improved greatly over time. Nowadays, it is possible to make a variety of objects more precisely and quickly in various sizes and colors using a wide variety of materials.

3D printers appear to be magical machines that can be used to make almost any object without much trouble or cost. However, the **versatility**《多用途性》 of these machines, if used for **sinister**《邪悪な》 purposes, may lead to **nightmares**《悪夢》. Since it is even possible to make guns and other weapons with 3D printers, strict rules are needed to properly regulate the use of this technology.

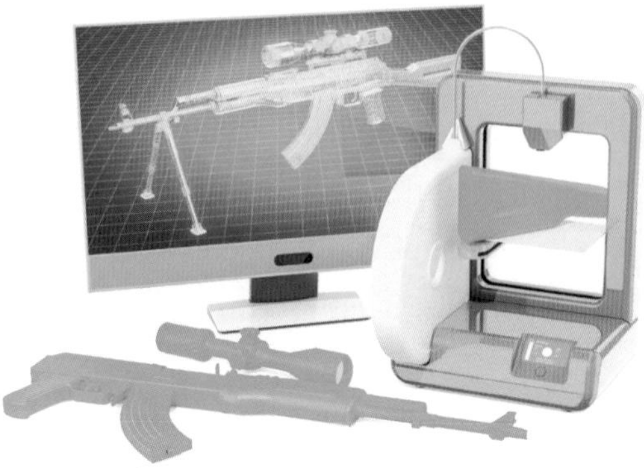

6. *Understanding 3D printing Key terms* 3Dプリントを考えるのに必要な用語

Practice 8 **Discuss the key terms on 3D printing: additive manufacturing, injection molding, 3D graphics, and 3D visualization software.**

Additive manufacturing

3D printing is a type of additive manufacturing. It is a process by which three-dimensional objects are made by stacking thin layers of material one on top of another.

Injection molding

Injection molding《射出成形》 is a process for making plastic parts. Various products are manufactured using this process, which involves injecting **molten material**《溶解金属》 into a **die**《金型》 made from a block of aluminum or steel. The input materials are usually **polymer beads**《ポリマービーズ》 that are melted in a heating cylinder prior to injection. After injection, the die is cooled and the polymers harden into the shape of the mold. The finished part is then removed.

Injection molding

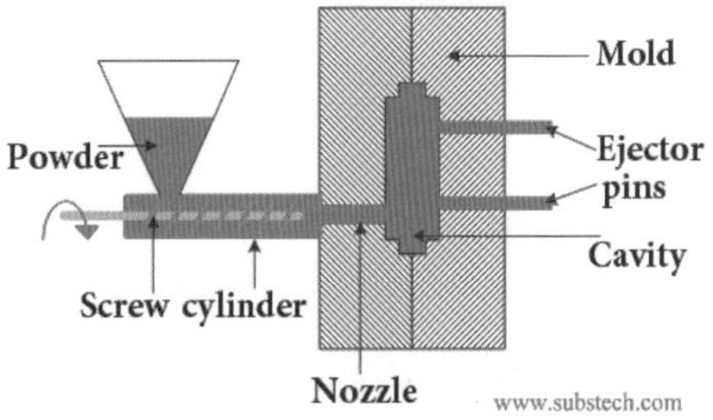

3D graphics

3D graphics software has many applications. Besides its use in the design of real-world objects for 3D printing, CAD software is also used by gaming artists who can create complex virtual worlds and characters.

3D visualization software

3D visualization is the process of creating graphics and **rendering designs**《完成予想描画》 using 3D software. Architectural and engineering firms, as well as those in the film and gaming industries, make extensive use of 3D **visualization software**《可視化ソフトウェア》.

7. Learning outcomes What have you learned? 学んだことの整理

Self-assessment 自己評価をしよう

I can listen to and read **what 3D printing is.**	0---30---50---70---100%
I can speak and write about **how 3D printing works.**	0---30---50---70---100%
I can understand **the ideas and problems about 3D printing.**	0---30---50---70---100%

Practice 9 **A summary of learning: write a summary of what you have learned in this unit.**

Key terms

Key sentences

Key facts

Your understanding

Your thoughts

Unit 3

Power electronics supporting our life

私たちの生活を支えるパワーエレクトロニクス

1. *CLIL attainment target*　この課の学習目標を確認しよう

1. I can listen to and read **what power electronics is.**　聞く・読む技能
2. I can speak and write about **how power electronics makes our life better.**　話す・書く技能
3. I can understand **the ideas and problems about power electronics.**　関連の内容の理解

2. *Introduction　What is power electronics?*　パワーエレクトロニクスとは何か？

Practice 1　Listen and check your understanding　聞き取ってみよう　12

1) What kind of problem does Jane have while building a robot?

a) switches　b) tasks　c) power limitations

2) What does Yoko suggest that Jane should do to solve the problem?

a) change small transistors　b) check switches　c) use power transistors

Practice 2　Read and check your understanding　情報を理解しよう　13

Power electronics refers to the use of solid-state electronics to control and convert electrical power. It is an important technology with practical applications across a wide range of fields. **Power conversion technology**《電力変換技術》 using **semiconductor devices**《半導体素子》 is a key specialty. Many electrical appliances, such as refrigerators, washing machines, and air conditioners, rely on power electronics to efficiently control, convert, and utilize electrical energy. Recently, the widespread use of LEDs has produced energy savings, and electric and hybrid vehicles have attracted much attention as innovative examples of modern-day power electronics technology.

Practice 3　Talk in pairs　内容を確認して、英語でおしゃべりしよう

Do you know where power electronic applications are used?

e.g.　A: We are now studying power electronics. It is used in many applications.
B: Mobile phones use this technology, right?
A: Well, I'm not sure. Let's do some research.

3. *Topic 1* *Two forms of electricity* 電気の2つの形式 14

Practice 4 **What impact will more efficient electricity use have on the world?**
電気の効率的な使用は世の中にどのようなインパクトを与えますか?

1. Electricity is the set of physical phenomena relating to electric charge. The most important is electric current, which occurs when electric charge in the form of individual electrons move through a conductor, such as a **copper wire**《銅線》. There are two types of electric current: **direct current**《直流》 **(DC)** and **alternating current**《交流》 **(AC)**. The difference between DC and AC lies in how the charges flow.

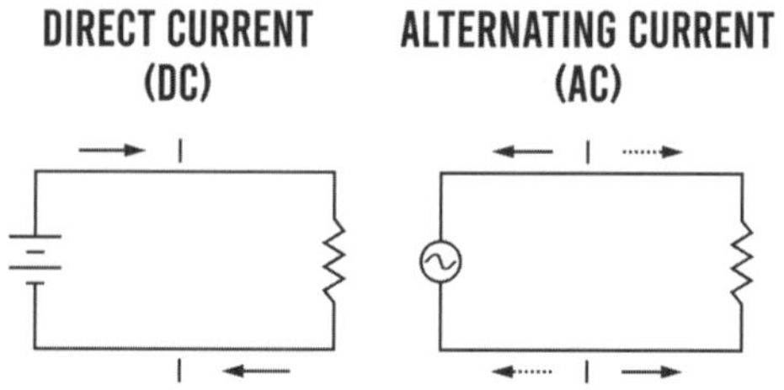

2. DC is a stream of charges that always flows in the same direction. Most portable electronic devices use DC for internal power, so an AC to DC converter is placed inside the device's power charger to convert AC to DC.
3. AC is a stream of charges that reverses directions. AC supplied by a typical household outlet is in the form of a **sinusoidal wave**《正弦波》, whose frequency is different between 50 Hz in eastern Japan and 60 Hz in western Japan.
4. There are four types of electrical power conversion: 1) DC to DC, 2) DC to AC, 3) AC to DC, and 4) AC to AC. In DC to DC conversion, the current and voltage values change from the input side to the output side. In DC to AC conversion, the **waveform**《波形》 varies greatly from linear to sinusoidal. In AC to DC conversion, **rectifier diodes**《整流ダイオード》 are used to prevent the voltage from reversing polarity in a process known as **rectification**《整流》. Finally, in AC to AC conversion, frequency changes in addition to the current and voltage values.
5. Electrical devices that convert currents are called converters, rectifiers, and inverters. A DC-to-DC convertor changes a source of direct current from one voltage to another. An AC-to-AC converter changes one AC waveform to another. A rectifier converts AC to DC, adjusting voltage or frequency in the process, and an inverter converts DC to AC.
6. A power converter with a semiconductor switch can be turned on and off. It is faster than one with a mechanical switch. Also, since semiconductor switches are tiny, their use has led to rapid miniaturization of electronic devices, such as TVs and smartphones.

4. *Text summarization How to make a summary* 必要な情報のまとめ方

Practice 5 **Summary of Topic 1 Recite it** Topic 1（前ページ）のまとめ 暗唱しよう

1. Electricity is the set of physical phenomena relating to electric charge.
2. DC is a stream of charges that always flows in the same direction.
3. AC is a stream of charges that reverses directions.
4. There are four types of electrical power conversion.
5. Electrical devices that convert currents are called converters, rectifiers, and inverters.
6. A power converter with a semiconductor switch can be turned on and off.

Practice 6 **Read and summarize** 読んで内容を把握してサマリーを作成しよう 15

Electronic devices using semiconductor technology can be switched at high speed. Also, the use of semiconductor components facilitates the miniaturization of electronic devices.

AC flows from **household outlets**《家庭用コンセント》, but DC is needed to charge batteries. Thus, it is necessary to convert or rectify AC to DC and properly adjust voltage before charging batteries contained within smartphones, laptop PCs, and other devices. There are advantages to using semiconductor components. The size and weight of **transformers**《変圧器》 can be greatly reduced. In conventional AC to DC conversion, voltage is first lowered by a transformer, and then current is rectified by a diode and smoothed by a **capacitor**《キャパシタ》.

Power electronics technology is greatly useful in motor drive technologies, such as electric cars, hybrid cars, and trains. It supports our lives in various places, such as power saving and high performance of air conditioners and PCs. Wireless power supply technology enables the charging of batteries without cables. Due to advancements in **wireless power transfer**《ワイヤレス電力伝送》, it is possible to transmit electric power across space using time-varying electromagnetic fields. As a result, you can charge your mobile phone without using a connecting cable.

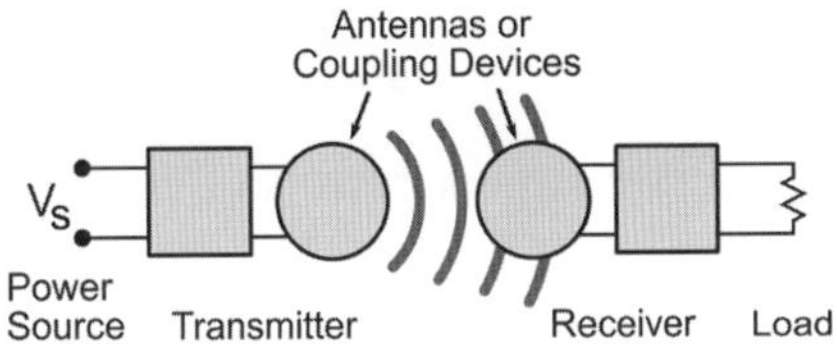

Complete the summary 適切な語を入れてサマリーを完成しよう

Electronic devices using semiconductor technology can be switched at (   ) speed. AC flows from (   ) outlets, but DC is needed to charge batteries. There are advantages to using (   ) components. Power (   ) technology is greatly useful in motor drive technologies. (   ) power supply technology enables the charging of batteries without cables.

Research **What are you interested in when reading this passage? Choose one and do research.**

5. *Topic 2 The future of power electronics* パワーエレクトロニクスの未来

16

Practice 7 **What do you expect about the future use of power electronics? Share ideas in groups.** パワーエレクトロニクスはどのようになると思いますか？

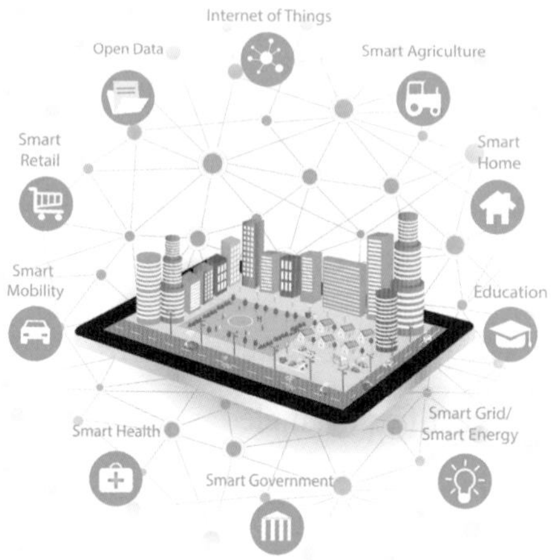

Power electronics was academically defined by William Newell in 1973, though the term had been used before. He combined three major **disciplines**《分野》 of electrical engineering: power, electronics, and control. Since then, remarkable progress has been made in the industrial world.

Advancements in power electronics technology makes electronic products smaller. It also helps reduce power consumption. With the **advent**《出現》 of wireless power transfer, it is now even possible to charge electronic devices wirelessly. This will help create a **ubiquitous**《どこにでもある》 network society, in which people can use and charge their portable devices without cables.

The extent to which《～する程度》 a device can be **downsized**《小型化する》 often depends upon how small its power conversion circuit can be made. In cases that a device's size is held constant, performance improvements are usually possible. Smartphones, for example, are not only highly compact and **lightweight**《軽量の》. Nevertheless, over successive product **iterations**《反復》, their performance often improves, too.

Power electronics plays a key role in new electrical engineering technologies. For example, it is used within **photovoltaic power stations**《太陽光発電所》, also known as solar parks, to generate large amounts of environmentally clean energy. So, power electronics has many diverse applications.

In the future, power electronics will likely expand beyond the traditional engineering fields. It will also form greater connections with other fields such as chemistry, robotics, and **superconductivity**《超伝導》.

6. *Understanding power electronics Key terms*

パワーエレクトロニクスを考えるのに必要な用語

Practice 8 **Discuss the key terms on power electronics: electric current, rectifier, voltage, and power electronics devices.**

Electric current

Current is the flow of electrons through a conducting material. The direction of the flow is from positive to negative potential, but the electrons actually flow in the opposite direction. The **Ampere**《アンペア》 is used as the standard unit of electric current.

Rectifier

A rectifier is an electrical device that converts AC to DC. The process is called rectification since it "straightens" the direction of the current. Rectifiers typically contain diodes, which function as one-way valves, permitting electric current to flow only in one direction. Besides diodes, rectifiers also contain **thyristors**《半導体整流素子：サイリスタ》 which help control the rectification function.

Voltage

Voltage is the difference in electric potential between two points. If two points with different electric potential are joined via a conducting material (such as a wire), then a circuit is formed and electrons flow, resulting in an electric current. The units of voltage are called volts (V).

Power electronics devices

Power electronics devices act as switches and have two modes: on and off. In "on" mode, the switch is closed. This means there is no voltage drop across them and current flows through them easily. In "off" mode, the switch is open. In this case, there is a full voltage drop across them and no current flows through them.

7. *Learning outcomes* *What have you learned?* 学んだことの整理

Self-assessment 自己評価をしよう

I can listen to and read **what power electronics is.**	0---30---50---70---100%
I can speak and write about **how power electronics makes our life better.**	0---30---50---70---100%
I can understand **the ideas and problems about power electronics.**	0---30---50---70---100%

Practice 9 **A summary of learning: write a summary of what you have learned in this unit.**

Key terms

Key sentences

Key facts

Your understanding

Your thoughts

Technology column 1: a history of engineering

17

Discuss what you learned about it and what you want to know about it.

When and how did the **discipline**《分野》 of engineering emerge?

People had lived a simple life before the rise of modern **civilizations**《文明》. It is thought that early humans began to use fire and settle near rivers to have easy access to water about 400,000 years ago. As they became more **civilized**《文明化する》, they began to develop and use tools to make their lives more **comfortable**《快適な》. In Rome during the 4th century B.C., people who built convenient tools and facilities such as metal hammers and water systems were called engineers.

The modern occupation of an engineer began in the 16th century, when some people began using mathematics to design **military fortifications**《軍事要塞》. In the 19th century, many methods of treating iron and oil were invented, and scientists and inventors developed many technologies. For example, Andrew Hallidie invented the San Francisco cable car in 1873, and Alexander Graham Bell **patented**《特許をとった》 the telephone in 1876. Engineering **specializations**《専門性》, including **civil engineering**《土木工学》, mechanical engineering and electrical engineering, had begun to emerge by that time. As a result, engineering, which had been a **master-apprentice**《徒弟制度》 system until then, became **systematized**《体系化する》. The Massachusetts Institute of Technology, a world-famous **institution**《研究機関》 specializing in science and engineering research and education, began with 15 students in 1865.

In the 20th century, engineering provided our life necessities, new sources of energy, and modern conveniences such as **transportation**《輸送》 and information networks. Now, in the 21st century, **information and communication technology (ICT)**《情報通信技術》 enables many people to learn online and work remotely. To develop practical solutions that **enrich**《豊かにする》 people's lives, engineers still need technical knowledge as well as an understanding of human beings and society.

Paragraph writing about Technology column 1

What did you learn about this topic?

What do you want to know more about this topic?

Unit 4

Eco-housing for a better life

より良い生活に向けたエコハウス

1. *CLIL attainment target*　この課の学習目標を確認しよう

1. I can listen to and read **what eco-housing is.**　聞く・読む技能
2. I can speak and write **how eco-housing works.**　話す・書く技能
3. I can understand **the ideas and problems about eco-housing.**　関連の内容の理解

2. *Introduction　What is eco-housing?*　エコハウスとは何か？

Practice 1　Listen and check your understanding　聞き取ってみよう　18

1) Which is a good point about eco-housing?

a) saving energy　b) saving food　c) saving time

2) What is Takashi suggesting to Jane when she is trying to find an eco-house?

a) saving energy　b) making it cost-effective　c) sharing it with him

Practice 2　Read and check your understanding　情報を理解しよう　19

Climate change due to global warming has become a serious problem worldwide. High temperatures and **sea level**《海抜》 rises are the signs of global warming. Global warming has led to many environmental problems, including higher temperatures, **gas emissions**《ガス排出》, and indoor uncomfortable conditions. Researchers now agree that one way of reducing the impact of global warming is to develop eco-housing.

Practice 3　Talk in pairs　内容を確認して、英語でおしゃべりしよう

What has climate change caused? What do you think about eco-housing?

e.g.　A: Do you want to live in an eco-house?

B: Yes, I do. I would like to protect nature. / No, I don't. It sounds expensive. I can't live there. / Well, yes and no. I don't know much about eco-housing, so I want to know a lot more.

A: I think global warming is not good. Eco-housing is a good idea.

3. *Topic 1*　*Eco-housing and green roof technology*　エコハウスとグリーンルーフ技術

Practice 4　**What are the characteristics of eco-housing?**　20

エコハウスにはどんな特徴があるでしょうか？

1. Eco-housing helps reduce indoor temperatures during the summer, which leads to lower energy consumption. We are living at a time when the earth is always affected by global warming and high levels of pollution. In order to make our lives better, the eco-housing approach has started.
2. Eco-houses use natural energy and water recycling systems to help lower energy costs. The use of natural energy reduces energy consumption and water recycling systems can help increase ground water levels. Even mechanical maintenance costs can be saved. Eco-housing can also help **absorb**《吸収する》 carbon dioxide (CO_2) from the **atmosphere**《大気》, which reduces the greenhouse effect.
3. Green roof technology is an example of an important eco-housing concept. It involves placing trees and plants on the roofs of buildings to form a roof garden. These living green roofs have many environmental benefits for buildings and the people who live in them. Such roofs can absorb rainwater, provide protection from sunlight, and help reduce air temperatures in cities.
4. Researchers at Columbia University's Center for Climate Systems Research have documented the positive impacts of green roof technology. These include the technology's ability to reduce a building's energy usage, **fossil fuel consumption**《化石燃料の消費》 and greenhouse gas emissions.

4. *Text summarization　How to make a summary*　必要な情報のまとめ方

Practice 5　Summary of Topic 1　Recite it　Topic 1（前ページ）のまとめ　暗唱しよう

1.	Eco-housing helps reduce indoor temperatures during the summer, which leads to lower energy consumption.
2.	Eco-houses use natural energy and water recycling systems to help lower energy costs.
3.	Green roof technology is an example of an important eco-housing concept.
4.	Researchers have documented the positive impacts of green roof technology.

Practice 6　Read and summarize　読んで内容を把握してサマリーを作成しよう　21

Houses are generally constructed with summer heat in Japan since it is more important to live comfortably in summer. There are four seasons in Japan. Winters are mild and summers are hot.

Also, 60% of houses in Japan are traditionally built from wood. One of the reasons is that Japan has many earthquakes and wooden buildings tend to be more **resilient**《耐震性》 to shaking than concrete or brick buildings.

Traditional Japanese houses use flooring coverings made from rice fiber called tatami. Many years ago, most Japanese people sat and slept on tatami, but today many prefer to sit on chairs, sleep on beds, and eat at tables, so tatami is not found in many urban homes.

Many houses in Japan have a **designated**《指定された》 area near the entrance where people remove and leave their shoes. The living area is separated from the entrance area with a raised wooden step. The difference in floor level shows the border between public and private space.

Complete the summary　適切な語を入れてサマリーを完成しよう

Houses are (　　　　) with summer heat in Japan since it is more important to live (　　　　) in summer. Also, (　　　　) % of houses in Japan are traditionally built from (　　　　). Traditional Japanese houses use flooring (　　　　) made from rice (　　　　) called tatami. Many houses in Japan have a (　　　　) area near the entrance where people remove and leave their (　　　　).

Research　**What are you interested in when reading this passage? Choose one and do research.**

5. *Topic 2 Benefits of eco-housing with green roofs*

22

グリーンルーフのエコハウスの利点

Practice 7 **There are some benefits of eco-housing with green roofs. Pick up some benefits and discuss how your life might change if you lived in this type of house.**

もしグリーンルーフのあるエコハウスに住んだら人々の生活はどう変わるでしょうか？

Building costs for an eco-house can be the same as, or lower than, those for a traditional house. Even when initial building costs are higher, the total cost over the lifecycle of an eco-house is usually lower than that of a traditional house. Moreover, eco-housing provides other financial benefits, such as lower operating costs due to less energy usage. Therefore, owners of eco-houses can enjoy the benefits of lower costs, lower risks, and longer building lifetimes.

Besides cost savings, eco-houses provide other benefits as well. The use of organic and **chemical-free building materials**《化学物質を含まない建材》 improves indoor air quality. Furthermore, natural lighting and natural temperature regulation help improve the health, comfort, and **well-being**《幸福感》 of **occupants**《居住者》. All of this leads to cleaner and healthier indoor environments that can increase the enjoyment and productivity for the people who live there.

Green roofs have many economic and environmental benefits. They can extend the lifespan of roofing materials and lower the costs of maintenance. Green roofs can also provide **a rainwater buffer**《雨水緩衝材》, **purify**《浄化する》 the air, and encourage **biodiversity**《生物多様性》. Moreover, they help lower a building's heating and cooling costs by regulating indoor temperatures naturally. Finally, green roofs can reduce the heat island effect and improve air quality in cities.

People who live and work in green buildings often discover that they are more comfortable than concrete surroundings. As a result, such occupants may feel more relaxed and less stress. In this way, green buildings may positively contribute to people's overall health and well-being.

6. *Understanding eco-housing Key terms*　エコハウスを考えるのに必要な用語

Practice 8　**Discuss the key terms on eco-housing: climate change, global warming, biodiversity, and eco-friendly.**

Climate change

Climate change refers to changes in global weather patterns and the effects that such changes have on the environment. It includes changes to oceans, **land surfaces**《地表》 and **ice sheets**《氷床》. These changes occur gradually over time and are measured by changes in **precipitation**《降水量》, temperature, and wind patterns.

Global warming

Global warming is the rise in global temperatures due to the increase of greenhouse gases in the atmosphere. It is primarily due to the human use of fossil fuels. Oil, coal and natural gas release carbon dioxide and other greenhouse gases into the air. These gases **trap**《閉じ込める》 heat within the atmosphere.

Biodiversity

Biodiversity is the variety of all living things including plants, animals, and **micro-organisms**《微生物》. The term is **a contraction of biological diversity**《生物多様性の短縮形》. It also refers to the number of different species which can live in a particular region. Therefore, areas with high levels of biodiversity are rich in biological resources.

Eco-friendly

Recently, the term 'eco-friendly' and its **synonyms**《同意語》, such as 'environmentally friendly,' 'nature friendly,' and 'green,' have become popular. What do these terms mean? In general, they describe something that is ecologically beneficial or, at least, not harmful to the environment. Many people today are aware of damage caused to the planet by human activity and consciously try to **minimize**《最小化する》 their own negative impact. As a result, they may prefer to buy and use 'eco-friendly' products designed to reduce the negative effects to the environment.

7. *Learning outcomes What have you learned?* 学んだことの整理

Self-assessment 自己評価をしよう

I can listen to and read **what eco-housing is**.	0---30---50---70---100%
I can speak and write **how eco-housing works**.	0---30---50---70---100%
I can understand **the ideas and problems about eco-housing**.	0---30---50---70---100%

Practice 9 **A summary of learning: write a summary of what you have learned in this unit.**

Key terms
Key sentences
Key facts
Your understanding
Your thoughts

Unit 5

Flow and the energy: fluid dynamics is useful in our life

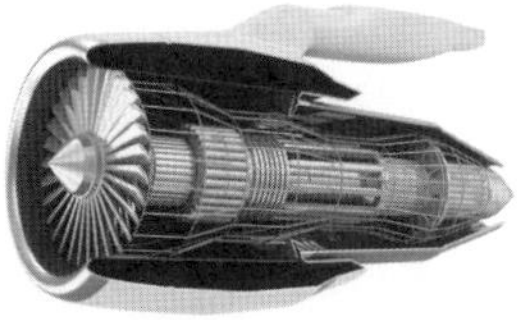

流れとエネルギー：流体力学は生活に役立つ

1. *CLIL attainment target*　この課の学習目標を確認しよう

1. I can listen to and read **what fluid dynamics is.**　聞く・読む技能
2. I can speak and write about **how fluid dynamics works.**　話す・書く技能
3. I can understand **the ideas and problems about fluid dynamics.**　関連の内容の理解

2. *Introduction　What is fluid dynamics?*　流体力学とは何か？

Practice 1　Listen and check your understanding　聞き取ってみよう　23

1) What is Yoko researching?

a) bullet trains　　b) flow and energy　　c) our daily life

2) What is Jane looking forward to tomorrow?

a) Yoko's presentation　　b) fluid dynamics　　c) her own presentation

Practice 2　Read and check your understanding　情報を理解しよう　24

Fluid dynamics is the study of fluids in motion. Fluids include liquids and gases and their movement is called "flow." Many kinds of flows exist in the world around us. For example, liquid flows can be seen in rivers and oceans in the form of currents, waves, and **tides**《潮流》. Airflows around moving vehicles, such as airplanes, trains, cars, and bicycles, affect their performance. Knowledge of fluid dynamics is necessary to study **tidal currents**《潮 流》, weather patterns, and **blood circulation**《血 流》. It can also be used to improve the design and **efficiency**《性能》 of things that people rely on, including air conditioners, cars, boats, and **wind turbines**《風力タービン》.

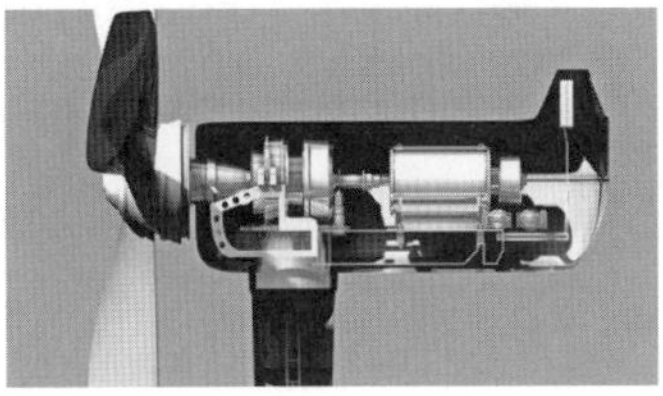

Practice 3　Talk in pairs　内容を確認して、英語でおしゃべりしよう

What is fluid dynamics?

e.g.　A: Are you interested in fluid dynamics?

B: Yes, sure. I like Shinkansen trains. If you see their shapes, you can understand fluid dynamics.

A: Really? I will look into them next. Thank you.

3. *Topic 1 The shape of the blades* ブレードの形状

Practice 4 **How does a wind turbine convert wind energy into electricity?** 25
風力タービンはどのようにして風力エネルギーを電気に変えるのですか?

1. A wind turbine **converts**《変換する》 wind energy into electricity through the use of large rotating **blades**《ブレード; 刃》. The shape and position of the blades **relative to**《〜に関連する》 the wind generate forces that cause the blades to rotate. You see the cross **sections**《断面》 of a blade on the right. Notice how the size and shape of the cross sections change along the length of the blade.

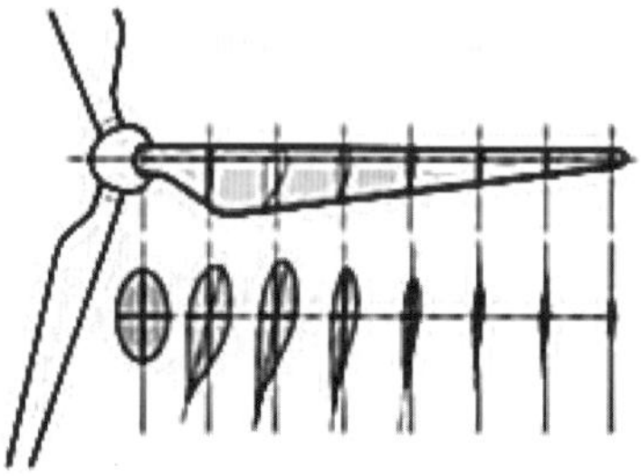

2. The air that flows around a blade **applies a force**《力をかける》 against it. The component of that force **perpendicular**《垂直の》 to the air flow is called **lift**《揚力》. Lift can be in any direction since it is a force defined relative to the direction of air flow, instead of the direction of gravity. In addition to lift, there is another force, called **drag**《抗力》, which always runs parallel to the direction of the air flow. Drag works against the blades and causes them to slow down.
3. An **airfoil**《翼》 is designed in a **streamlined shape**《流線型》 to maximize lift and minimize drag. Lift is generated by air flowing around an airfoil. A full explanation of how an airfoil works is complicated. You need to understand **conservation of mass**《質量保存の法則》, **momentum**《モーメント》, and energy function within **aerodynamics**《空気力学》. However, a simple explanation relies only on Newton's laws of motion and **Bernoulli's principle**《ベルヌーイの定理》.
4. A blade's airfoil shape causes air to move faster along its long edge, compared to its short edge. According to Bernoulli's principle, this faster moving air leads to reduced air pressure along the long edge. The **pressure difference**《圧力差》 along the edges helps create lift, which makes the blades spin.
5. The amount of lift and drag is affected by **the angle of attack (α)**《迎え角》. The blades are positioned relative to the wind at this angle.
It can be adjusted as needed.

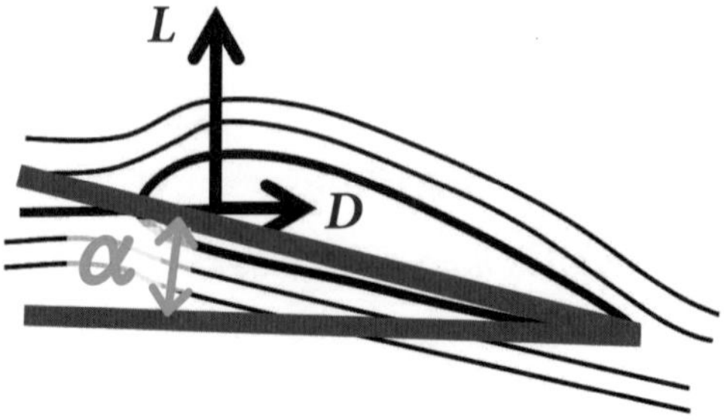

4. *Text summarization How to make a summary* 必要な情報のまとめ方

Practice 5 **Summary of Topic 1 Recite it** Topic 1（前ページ）のまとめ　暗唱しよう

1. A wind turbine converts wind energy into electricity through the use of large rotating blades.
2. The air that flows around a blade applies a force against it.
3. An airfoil is designed in a streamlined shape to maximize lift and minimize drag.
4. A blade's airfoil shape causes air to move faster along its long edge.
5. The amount of lift and drag is affected by the angle of attack (α).

Practice 6 **Read and summarize** 読んで内容を把握してサマリーを作成しよう 26

A fluid is anything that can float away or **spill**《こぼれる》 unless placed inside a **container**《容器》. When a fluid moves, the movement is called a flow. There are many different types of fluid flows. If the movement of a fluid doesn't change **over time**《時がたっても》, it is referred to as a **steady flow**《定常流》. When the flow is steady, fixed streamlines are used to represent the movement.

If the movement of a fluid keeps changing, then it is called an **unsteady flow**《非定常流》. When the flow is unsteady, at least one **variable**《変数》 at a **fixed point**《定点》 in the flow changes with time.

A smooth flow of a liquid is called a **laminar flow**《層流》. Imagine water flows out of a tap, for example. When the water flows straight down, it is a laminar flow.

An unsteady, irregular, and chaotic flow can be called a **turbulent flow**《乱流》. Unlike a laminar flow in which a liquid moves smoothly within layers, a turbulent flow is one in which a liquid mixes and flows irregularly between layers.

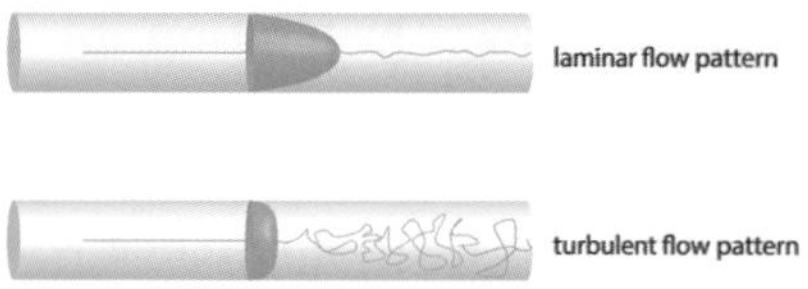

Complete the summary 適切な語を入れてサマリーを完成しよう

A fluid is anything that can float away or spill unless placed inside a (   ). If the movement of a fluid doesn't change over time, it is referred to as a (   ) flow. If the movement of a fluid keeps changing, it is called an (   ) flow. A smooth flow of liquid is called a (   ) flow. An unsteady, irregular, and chaotic flow can be called a (   ) flow.

Research **What are you interested in when reading this passage? Choose one and do research.**

5. Topic 2 The knowledge of fluid dynamics and energy from the wind turbine 流体力学の知識と風力タービンのエネルギー

27

Practice 7 **Efficient generation of energy is needed. But how? Do you think it is possible? Discuss how to efficiently generate electricity using the wind.**

風力を使ってどのようにして効果的に発電するのでしょうか？

There are two main forms of energy: **potential energy**《位置エネルギー》 and **kinetic energy**《運動エネルギー》, although energy can exist in many forms. Raising any object such as a hammer gives it potential energy. Dropping it to the floor converts that potential energy into kinetic energy.

Kinetic energy is the energy of **mass**《質量》 in motion and can be useful to produce electricity. Wind turbines, for example, are designed to convert kinetic energy in the wind into **mechanical energy**《力学的エネルギー》. How much kinetic energy can a wind turbine **harness**《利用する》?

Even the best **high-performance**《高性能》 turbines can harness 40 to 50% of the wind's kinetic energy. Actually, there is a theoretical limit known as the **Betz limit or Betz' law**《ベッツの法則》, which was formulated by the German **physicist**《物理学者》 Albert Betz. He concluded that wind turbines would never be able to convert more than 59.3% of the wind's kinetic energy into mechanical energy.

Blades are key factors which affect the **power output**《出力》 of wind turbines. The design of the blades affects their performance, which ultimately affects the efficiency of the turbine's **power generation**《発電》.

The efficiency of the blades depends on the lift that they produce and the drag and **torque**《トルク》 that they experience while turning. These factors are also influenced by other important variables, such as the size, shape, pitch, angle, and number of blades.

Nowadays, it is possible to visualize the airflow around wind turbine blades by using computer simulations. These tools help engineers gain a better understanding of fluid dynamics, which enables them to design and build more efficient wind turbines.

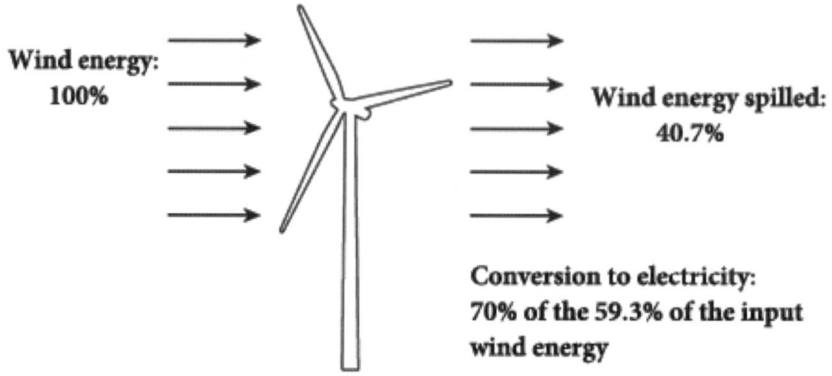

6. *Understanding fluid dynamics Key terms* 流体力学を考えるのに必要な用語

Practice 8 **Discuss the key terms on fluid dynamics: Archimedes' principle, fluid forces, and Computational Fluid Dynamics (CFD).**

Archimedes' principle

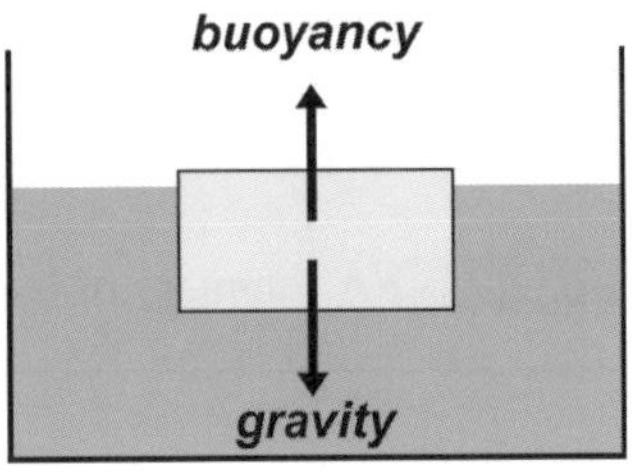

Archimedes' principle states that the **buoyancy force**《浮力》 **exerted**《力を及ぼす》 on an object is equal to the weight of the fluid that it displaces. This fundamental principle of buoyancy was discovered by Archimedes, a Greek physicist, mathematician, engineer, inventor, and astronomer. Buoyancy is an upward force exerted by a fluid on an object in a **gravitational field**《重力場》.

Fluid forces

There are four major forces that affect objects within fluid flows: **thrust**《推力》, weight, drag, and lift. Depending on the size and **velocity**《速度》 of an object relative to its surrounding fluid, these forces may or may not produce large effects. For large, fast-moving objects, such as cars, trains, ships, submarines, and airplanes, however, these forces have enormous effects. The thrust force moves something forward in the direction of motion. The weight force pulls toward the center of the earth. The drag force acts in the direction opposite of the **relative flow velocity**《相対流速》, and the lift force acts in the direction perpendicular to the relative flow.

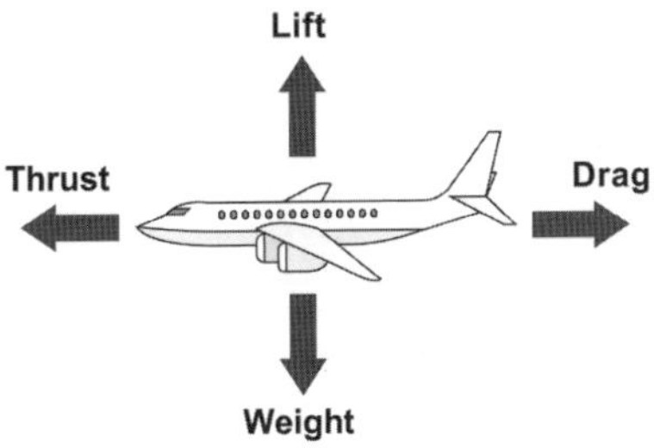

Computational Fluid Dynamics (CFD)

Computational Fluid Dynamics《数値流体力学》 (CFD) provides a **prediction**《予測》 of fluid flows by means of **mathematical modeling**《数理モデル》, **numerical analysis**《数値解析》, and software tools. Using CFD techniques, scientists and engineers create computer-based simulations in a **virtual flow laboratory**《バーチャル・フロー・ラボ》. CFD is best used in cases where it is hard to see the actual flow.

7. Learning outcomes *What have you learned?* 学んだことの整理

Self-assessment 自己評価をしよう

I can listen to and read **what fluid dynamics is.**	0---30---50---70---100%
I can speak and write about **how fluid dynamics works.**	0---30---50---70---100%
I can understand **the ideas and problems about fluid dynamics.**	0---30---50---70---100%

Practice 9 A summary of learning: write a summary of what you have learned in this unit.

Key terms

Key sentences

Key facts

Your understanding

Your thoughts

Unit 6

Electric vehicles (EVs): technology for assisting us

電気自動車：私たちを支える技術

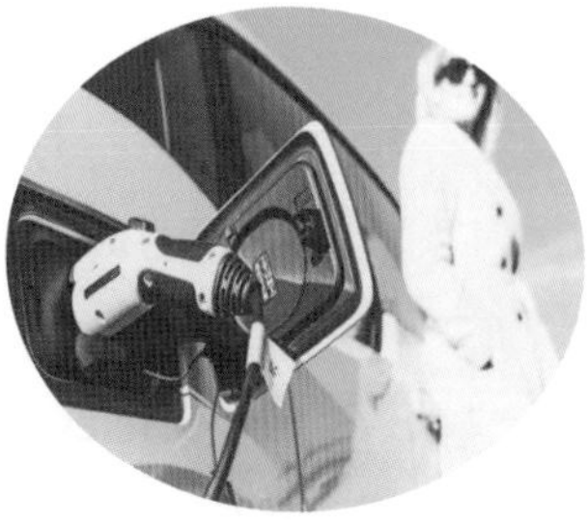

1. *CLIL attainment target*　この課の学習目標を確認しよう

1. I can listen to and read **what EVs are.**	聞く・読む技能
2. I can speak and write about **how EVs work.**	話す・書く技能
3. I can understand **the ideas and problems about EVs.**	関連の内容の理解

2. *Introduction*　*What are EVs?*　EVとは何か？

Practice 1 **Listen and check your understanding**　聞き取ってみよう　28

1) What do Yoko and her dad talk about?

a) grandpa's wheelchair　b) grandma's cleaner　c) grandpa's bike

2) What type of EV does Yoko's mother have?

a) a hybrid electric car　b) a vegetable cutter machine　c) an electric bike

Practice 2 **Read and check your understanding**　情報を理解しよう　29

Have you ever heard of an EV? EV stands for 'electric vehicle,' and refers to any vehicle with an electric motor. EV technology has been developed recently. That is because there are **environmental problems**《環境問題》 in the world today such as **global warming**《地球温暖化》 and **air pollution**《大気汚染》. **Electrification**《電化》 of vehicles is a good way to reduce **emissions**《排出》 of **exhaust gases**《排気ガス》 such as CO_2. Such **reductions**《削減》 are necessary in order to save the Earth's natural environment for the future.

Practice 3 **Talk in pairs**　内容を確認して、英語でおしゃべりしよう

Which electric vehicles are you familiar with?

e.g.　A: Would you like to have an EV?

B: I'm not sure. My family has a hybrid car. How about you?

A: I use an electric bike since it's useful for climbing a long, steep road on my way to school.

3. *Topic 1* *Types and components of EVs* EVのタイプと構成要素

Practice 4 **Do you think EVs can be a savior for our future life?** 30

EVは救世主となりえるでしょうか？

1. EVs are **vehicles**《車》 that run on electricity. They rely on electricity as their primary source of power. The electricity is stored in **onboard batteries**《車載バッテリー》. They can be repeatedly recharged with a cable connected to an electrical power source.

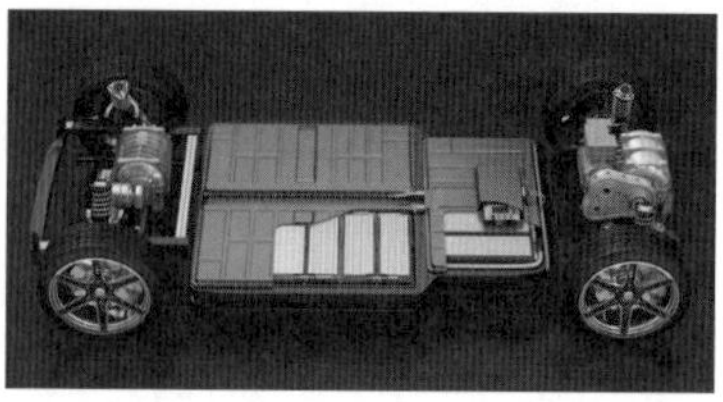

2. EVs are usually powered by electric motors, but they sometimes have **multiple motors**《複数のモーター》. They use ordinary fuels such as gasoline or diesel, in addition to power from a battery.
3. There are three types of EVs: hybrid electric vehicles (HEVs), plug-in hybrid electric vehicles (PHEVs), and battery electric vehicles (BEVs).
4. HEVs are powered by both gasoline and electricity. The electricity is usually generated by the car's braking system, which converts kinetic energy into electrical power. The electrical power is then stored in an onboard battery and later used by the car's electric motor.
5. PHEVs have a large battery. They can be repeatedly recharged from an electrical power source. PHEVs can also use gasoline as an **alternative**《代替の》 source of power.
6. BEVs are the purest type of EVs. They use electricity as the only source of power. BEVs have rechargeable batteries, but no gasoline engines.
7. EVs have four **main components**《主要な構成要素》: a charger, a battery, a power control unit, and an electronic motor. An **accelerator pedal**《アクセルペダル》 is connected to a pair of **potentiometers**《ポテンショメーター；可変抵抗器》. They send a signal to the power control unit indicating the amount of power to deliver.
8. The components work together to obtain, store, deliver, and use power for the vehicle. First, a charger obtains and sends electric power to a battery. Whenever necessary, the power control unit then delivers electrical power from the battery to the electric motor. The motor then converts the power into mechanical motion.

4. *Text summarization How to make a summary* 必要な情報のまとめ方

Practice 5 **Summary of Topic 1 Recite it** Topic 1 (前ページ) のまとめ 暗唱しよう

1. EVs are vehicles that run on electricity.
2. EVs are usually powered by electric motors.
3. There are three types of EVs.
4. HEVs are powered by both gasoline and electricity.
5. PHEVs have a large battery.
6. BEVs are the purest type of EVs.
7. EVs have four main components.
8. The components work together to obtain, store, deliver, and use power for the vehicle.

Practice 6 **Read and summarize** 読んで内容を把握してサマリーを作成しよう 31

Besides **passenger cars**《乗用車》, there are other types of EVs which make our lives safer and more convenient. These exist in diverse fields, such as leisure, **welfare**《福祉》, and industry.

Each type of EV is designed for its own purpose. In the case of HEVs, a motor, an engine, and an **output power balance**《出力パワーバランス》 are selected to achieve best **performance**《性能》.

Some EVs simply help people move around more conveniently. These include electric bikes, electric wheelchairs, electric golf carts, and other types of personal transporters: electric skateboards, scooters, one or two-wheeled self-balancing vehicles, etc.

Other types of EVs are designed to help people do jobs more efficiently and safely. These include **electric harvesters**《電動収穫機》, electric vacuums used in airports or shopping malls, and automated guided vehicles in factories.

Electrification helps reduce people's **burden**《負担》, so it is likely that EVs will take on more essential roles within daily life in the future.

Complete the summary 適切な語を入れてサマリーを完成しよう

Besides passenger cars, there are other (　　　　) of EVs which make our lives (　　　　) and more convenient. Each type of EV is designed for its own (　　　　). Some EVs simply help (　　　　) move around more conveniently. Other types of EVs are designed to help people do (　　　　) more efficiently and safely. (　　　　) helps reduce people's burden.

Research **What are you interested in when reading this passage? Choose one and do research.**

5. Topic 2 Advantages and disadvantages of EVs EVの強みと弱み 32

Practice 7 **EVs seem to have advantages and disadvantages. Do you think EVs will be our main vehicles in the future? Discuss whether EV will surpass conventional cars or not.**

EVは従来の自動車を超えられるでしょうか？

EVs have become increasingly popular on streets and roads worldwide. Some people like EVs for their advantages, while others disregard them for their disadvantages.

First, in terms of advantages, EVs are very eco-friendly. When **compared with**《～と比較して》 conventional cars that consume gasoline or diesel, EVs **emit**《排出する》 few or no **exhaust gases**《排気ガス》 including CO_2. Also, EVs help conserve limited resources such as **fossil fuels**《化石燃料》 since they are powered mostly or exclusively by electricity.

Secondly, fuel costs for EVs are typically lower than conventional cars. That is because EVs use electricity, which is less expensive than gasoline and can be obtained from renewable sources. Moreover, since fossil fuels are limited in supply and costly to **extract**《抽出する》 from the Earth, the difference in cost between electricity and gasoline will likely increase in the future.

The third advantage of EVs is increased design **flexibility**《柔軟》. The main components of EVs typically require less space than a traditional engine and transmission. The extra space can be **utilized**《有効利用する》 for storage. For example, a BMW i3 has a **storage compartment**《収納区画》 under its **hood**《フード》 where a tire repair kit and power cord can be stored.

EVs have several disadvantages, such as their costs, their energy limitations, and their quiet operations. The initial purchase price, as well as repair and **maintenance costs**《維持費》, tends to be higher than those of conventional cars. Also, due to energy storage limitations of onboard batteries, EVs can run out of power when covering long distances. Since EVs operate quietly, they sometimes present a danger to **pedestrians**《歩行者》, who may not notice them approaching. Safety mechanisms such as alarm sensors must be developed to help solve this problem.

6. *Understanding EVs* *Key terms* EVを考えるのに必要な用語

Practice 8 **Discuss the key terms on EVs: Regenerative braking, DC, AC, and Power Control Units (PCUs).**

Regenerative braking

Regenerative braking《回生ブレーキ》 is an EV technology that uses a vehicle's braking system to create and store electric power in the batteries. In an EV, energy flows from the batteries to an electric motor which drives the wheels. When the brakes are applied, energy flows from the wheels back to the batteries via the motor, which acts as an **electric generator**《発電機》. **Subsequently**《続いて》, when the accelerator pedal is pressed, energy stored while braking can be reused.

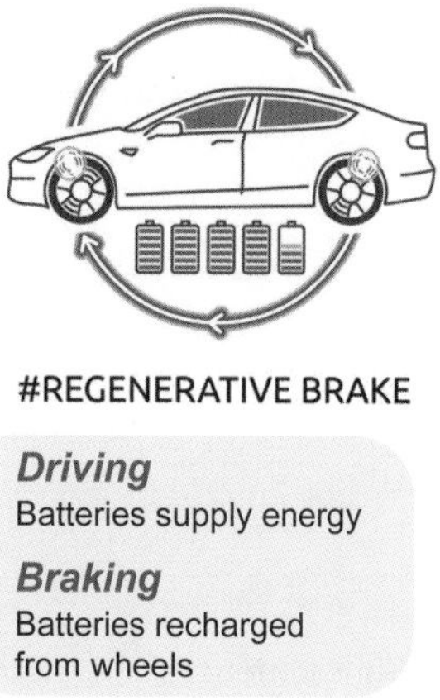

DC, AC

EVs run by sending electricity from a battery to a motor. The battery uses a circuit requiring DC (direct current) and the motor uses a circuit requiring AC (alternating current). EVs are equipped with **converters**《変換器》 for switching DC to AC. Likewise, another converter that switches AC to DC is used in order to charge the battery using a standard outlet.

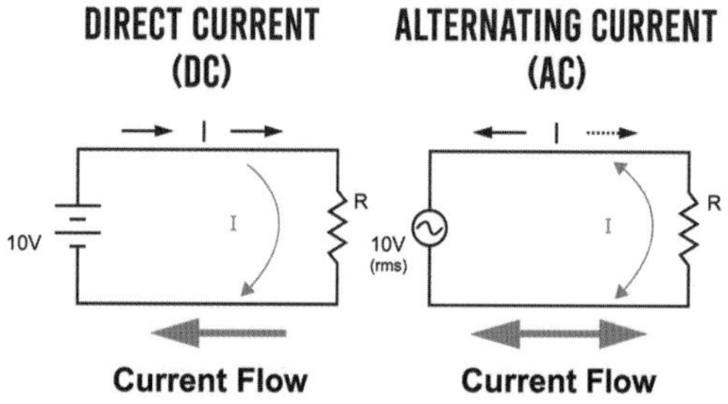

Power Control Units (PCUs)

Automobile manufacturers design and develop **Power Control Units (PCUs)**《電力制御装置》 for use in **motor-driven hybrid**《モーター駆動のハイブリッド》 and electric vehicles. A PCU includes two main components: an inverter to power the motor and a boost converter to increase **voltage**《電圧》.

7. Learning outcomes What have you learned? 学んだことの整理

Self-assessment 自己評価をしよう

I can listen to and read **what EVs are**.	0---30---50---70---100%
I can speak and write about **how EVs work**.	0---30---50---70---100%
I can understand **the ideas and problems about EVs**.	0---30---50---70---100%

Practice 9 A summary of learning: write a summary of what you have learned in this unit.

Key terms

Key sentences

Key facts

Your understanding

Your thoughts

Technology column 2: Saving energy

33

Discuss what you learned about it and what you want to know about it.

Since the Great East Japan Earthquake in 2011, Japan has been trying to reduce its **dependence**《依存》 on nuclear power and rely more on renewable energy sources. As of 2017, Japan sources 39% of its energy from oil, 23.4% from LNG, 25.1% from coal, 1.4% from nuclear power, and 11.1% from renewable sources, such as solar, wind, hydroelectric, and geothermal power. Since fossil fuels make up 87.4% of the total, Japan relies almost entirely on fossil fuels for power generation.

Widespread use of fossil fuels **accelerates**《加速させる》 global warming and brings about climate change. This causes the **flooding**《洪水》 of islands and other serious damage due to extreme weather events such as typhoons. In Japan, **mega-solar power plants**《メガソーラー発電所》 are being built due to the growing need for **alternative**《代替の》 energy sources, though there is a potential risk of landslides in **mountainous**《山岳の》 areas.

While switching to renewable energy sources is one way to solve energy problems, it is also important to reduce the power consumption of everyday devices. For example, **incandescent**《白熱の》 light bulbs are highly inefficient, since much of the electrical energy is converted into heat. In fact, only 10% of the energy is converted into visible light, but the remaining 90% of energy is invisible light including infrared light and ultraviolet light. LEDs, on the other hand, do not convert heat into light like incandescent bulbs. Instead, they use semiconductor materials to convert electrical energy directly into light, which is mostly visual ray. LEDs convert electrical energy into light more efficiently than incandescent bulbs and help save electricity.

Inventions《発明》 that increase the efficiency of energy conversion such as LEDs can help solve current energy problems. Although power generation methods receive a lot of attention, it is also important that engineers focus on creating solutions that use energy efficiently. Such a **dual-focused**《二重の》 approach is necessary to solve environmental issues.

Paragraph writing about Technology column 2

What did you learn about this topic?

What do you want to know more about this topic?

Unit 7

Rescue robots as substitutes in danger

危険状況で人に代わる救助ロボット

1. *CLIL attainment target* この課の学習目標を確認しよう

1. I can listen to and read **what rescue robots are.** 聞く・読む技能
2. I can speak and write about **how rescue robots work.** 話す・書く技能
3. I can understand **the ideas and problems about rescue robots.** 関連の内容の理解

2. *Introduction What are rescue robots?* レスキューロボットとは何か？

Practice 1 Listen and check your understanding 聞き取ってみよう 34

1) What are Jane and Kevin talking about?

a) care robots b) cleaning robots c) rescue robots

2) What does Kevin like to do?

a) creating robots b) cleaning robots c) cleaning a floor

Practice 2 Read and check your understanding 情報を理解しよう 35

Rescue robots are designed for rescuing people and sometimes animals. These robots must work in places that are unsafe for humans to enter, including disaster areas that are excessively hot, **polluted**《汚染した》, or contain low levels of oxygen. In Japan, natural disasters such as earthquakes, heavy rains, floods, volcanic **eruptions**《噴火》, tsunamis, and typhoons, occur frequently. These disasters often produce secondary disasters such as fires, **landslides**《地滑り》, and polluted areas. Rescue robots can work in these disaster environments to help people.

Practice 3 Talk in pairs 内容を確認して、英語でおしゃべりしよう

What kind of rescue robots do you know about?

e.g. A: I'm not sure, but I think drones can be rescue robots.
B: Yes, I think so. Drones might be used to find or help people in difficult situations.
A: That's right. I agree with you.

3. *Topic 1* *Requirements for rescue robots* レスキューロボットに求められること

Practice 4 **Can you separate what humans do from what machines do?** 36
人間がすることと機械がすることは分けられますか？

1. Rescue robots are typically classified according to their capabilities. There are various types of rescue robots that can fly, swim, walk, run, roll, or crawl.
2. There are three challenges associated with the development of rescue robots at the moment. The first challenge is to develop rescue robots' information and communication technology skills. The second challenge is to improve their **mobility**《可動性》. The third is to improve their **manipulation**《操作》 skills.
3. In 2015, **the United States Defense Research Projects Agency**《国防高等研究計画局》 **(DARPA)** held a **competition**《競争》 in which teams of engineers from around the world took part. The DARPA Robotic Challenge required each team to design and construct a robot that could complete a series of tasks on an obstacle course. All tasks, including a drive task, a wall task, a rubble task, and a stairs task, had to be completed within 60 minutes. Human operators had to rely entirely on their robots' sensors to know what was happening while their robots were on the course.

4. **Accelerometers**《加速度計》 help rescue robots manage speed effectively and navigate safely. This device helps rescue robots **gauge**《測定する》 their speed and acceleration. When moving through **debris**《デブリ(がれき)》, the robots may need to move slowly to avoid falling down.
5. **Gyroscope**《ジャイロスコープ》 sensors play a role in helping rescue robots maintain their balance. As disaster areas are often filled with debris, it may be necessary for a robot to change the direction of its movement frequently. When doing so, it must maintain balance. The ability to maintain balance is a key requirement for rescue robots.

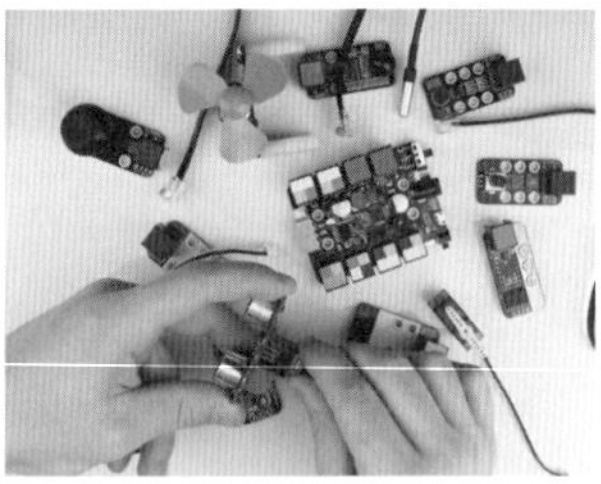

6. Some rescue robots use 3D laser scanners to create detailed maps of their surroundings. Such detailed maps are important since they enable rescue staff to better plan and coordinate rescue operations.
7. Robotic hands enable rescue robots to hold and manipulate objects. To assist rescue staff in disasters, rescue robots need to be able to pick up and remove lots of things. They must grip sensitively, **detect**《見つける》 pressure, and move debris carefully.

4. *Text summarization How to make a summary* 必要な情報のまとめ方

Practice 5 **Summary of Topic 1 Recite it** Topic 1（前ページ）のまとめ 暗唱しよう

1. Rescue robots are typically classified according to their capabilities.
2. There are three challenges associated with the development of rescue robots at the moment.
3. The United States Defense Research Projects Agency (DARPA) held a competition.
4. Accelerometers help rescue robots manage speed effectively and navigate safely.
5. Gyroscope sensors play a role in helping rescue robots maintain their balance.
6. Some rescue robots use 3D laser scanners to create detailed maps of the surroundings.
7. Robotic hands enable rescue robots to hold and manipulate objects.

Practice 6 **Read and summarize** 読んで内容を把握してサマリーを作成しよう 37

In Japan, natural disasters, such as earthquakes, heavy rains, floods, volcanic eruptions, tsunamis, and typhoons, occur frequently. Such disasters often produce fires, landslides, and polluted areas. Japan has many disaster victims. According to the UN Office for Disaster Risk Reduction (UNDRR), disasters in 2018 affected more than 60 million people worldwide and resulted in a death toll of 10,733. With 1,599,497 people affected by disasters, Japan ranked as the ninth worst **disaster-laden**《災害に打ちひしがれた》 country that year. Large disasters can cause secondary disasters. For example, large earthquakes frequently cause fires. Such fires produce intense heat and harmful gases that **endanger**《危険にさらす》 people who are escaping. These secondary disasters increase the risks associated with primary disasters.

The damaged nuclear power plants in Fukushima face **decommissioning**《廃炉にすること》. There is still a lot of polluted debris in the nuclear plants, so Japan will have to overcome the problem. Nuclear decommissioning is a process in which a nuclear power plant site is **dismantled**《解体される》 and no longer needs **radiation protection**《放射能防護》.

Complete the summary 適切な語を入れてサマリーを完成しよう

In Japan, natural (　　　　), such as earthquakes, volcanic eruptions, tsunamis, and typhoons, (　　　) frequently. Japan has many disaster (　　　　). Big disasters can cause (　　　　　) disasters. The damaged nuclear power plants in Fukushima face (　　　　　　).

Research **What are you interested in when reading this passage? Choose one and do research.**

5. Topic 2 Knowledge and functions of rescue robots

38

レスキューロボットの機能と知識

Practice 7 **How do you feel when earthquakes happen? Or have you experienced other disasters before?** 地震の時にあなたはどう感じますか、また他の災害に被災したことがありますか?

Japan has focused not only on accident prevention but also on disaster preparedness, since the Great Hanshin Awaji Earthquake in 1995. Advances in robotic technology has led to the development of rescue robots, which are designed to work in disaster areas. People now rely on such robots in rescue and recovery operations.

Rescue robots must operate in disaster areas where there is a lot of rubble. Since such environments are **unpredictable**《予測できない》, the robots must be able to move around on their own. To meet these requirements, engineers have developed different types of robots, each of which has its own special characteristics.

Two examples of rescue robots are the robotic crawler and the multi-legged robot. A crawler has a high **ground-covering**《地面を動く能力》 ability and uses fixed sensors. A multi-legged robot, on the other hand, can travel farther than a crawler, but needs multi-actuators, which are harder to control.

A semi-autonomous《半自律的》 robot equipped with sensors can acquire spatial information, such as the location and distance of objects or the height of steps. This information helps the robot move itself to a specific **destination**《目的地》.

Robotic crawlers containing sensors can assess ground conditions. This ability helps them **maneuver**《操作する》 within **treacherous**《不安定な》 areas. Similarly, multi-legged robots gather data through sensors. The data is used to calculate the motion that the robot must perform to produce the best position for the next step. In both cases, operators only need to specify the direction in which to move the robot. The robots then navigate through rubble and climb up steps **autonomously**《自律的に》.

Technology used by rescue robots has developed greatly since the first rescue robot contest was held in Japan in 2000. In that contest, teams had to rescue dolls buried in debris using their robots.

6. *Understanding rescue robots Key terms* レスキューロボットを考えるのに必要な用語

Practice 8 **Discuss the key terms on rescue robots: actuator, sensor and algorithm.**

Actuator

An actuator is a device that converts energy into mechanical motion. There are several actuators which are used for rescue robots, including servomotors, stepper motors, and **hydraulic**《油圧の》 actuators.

Sensor

A sensor is a device that detects or measures something and converts it into a signal. Using such signal data, rescue robots can identify various physical **properties**《特性》, including the size and weight of objects, as well as the temperature and pressure of their surroundings. These attributes enable robots to sense their environment as humans do. To gather such data, many kinds of sensors have been developed and are now in use. For example, **piezoelectric**《圧電性の》 elements are used to feel pressure.

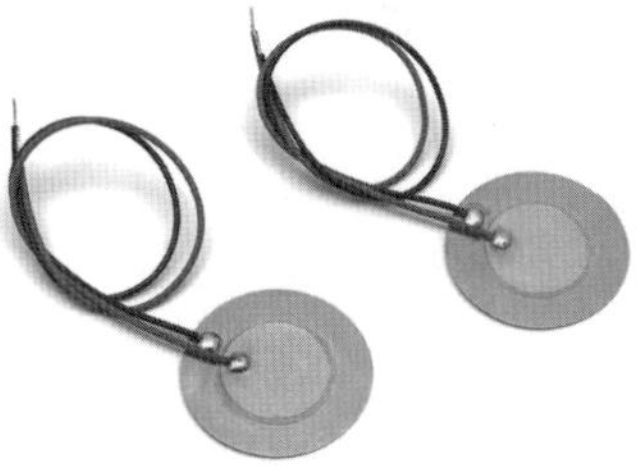

Algorithm

An algorithm is a process or set of rules designed to solve a problem. Rescue robots utilize algorithms to perform complex jobs. A cooking recipe illustrates the idea of an algorithm. It gives a step-by-step procedure for cooking food. To cook pasta, for example, a person must:

1. put water into a pot
2. heat the pot until the water boils
3. add pasta to the boiling water
4. add some salt for flavor
5. **stir**《かき混ぜる》 and periodically check until the pasta is al dente
6. **strain**《ピンと延ばす》

The above tasks, taken together, make up the algorithm for cooking pasta.

7. Learning outcomes What have you learned? 学んだことの整理

Self-assessment 自己評価をしよう

I can listen to and read **what rescue robots are**.	0---30---50---70---100%
I can speak and write about **how rescue robots work**.	0---30---50---70---100%
I can understand **the ideas and problems about rescue robots**.	0---30---50---70---100%

Practice 9 A summary of learning: write a summary of what you have learned in this unit.

Key terms

Key sentences

Key facts

Your understanding

Your thoughts

Unit 8

Nanotechnology to change our life

生活を変えるナノテクノロジー

1. *CLIL attainment target*　この課の学習目標を確認しよう

1. I can listen to and read **what nanotechnology is.**　聞く・読む技能
2. I can speak and write about **how nanotechnology changes our life.**　話す・書く技能
3. I can understand **the ideas and problems about nanotechnology.**　関連の内容の理解

2. *Introduction　What is nanotechnology?*　ナノテクノロジーとは何か？

Practice 1　Listen and check your understanding　聞き取ってみよう　39

1) What makes Yoko hesitate about swimming?
   a) nanoparticles　b) getting sunburned　c) sunscreens
2) What makes Yoko dcecide to go swimming?
   a) nanoparticles　b) getting sunburned　c) sunscreens

＊ nanoparticles ナノ粒子

Practice 2　Read and check your understanding　情報を理解しよう　40

"Nano" is a **prefix**《接頭辞》 that means one billionth (1/1,000,000,000). A nanometer is one billionth of a meter, 0.000000001 or 10^{-9} meters. Nanotechnology is, **simply speaking**《簡単に言うと》, super small science. It is the study and **application**《応用》 of extremely small things which can be used in many science fields, such as materials science, engineering, physics, chemistry, and biology. Many people who like sports may think of it as a technology that makes **athletic equipment**《スポーツ用品》, such as shoes and rackets, stronger and lighter.

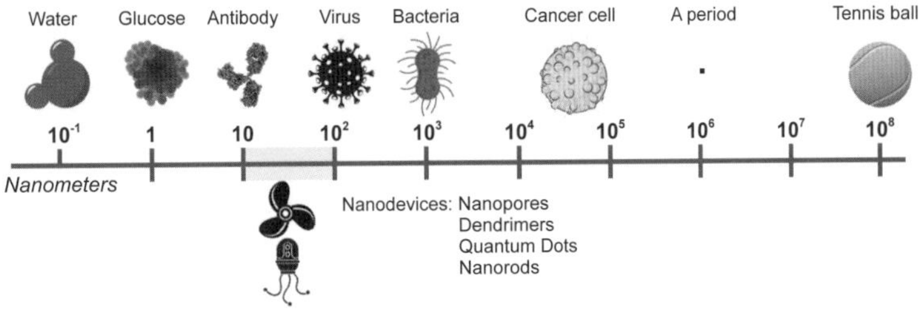

Practice 3　Talk in pairs　内容を確認して、英語でおしゃべりしよう

What does "nanotechnology" mean? Where is nanotechnology used around you?

e.g.　A: Are you interested in nanotechnology?
B: Yes, I am. Nanotechnology is very useful. / No, I'm not. It sounds dangerous.
A: Why do you think so?

3. *Topic 1* *History of nanotechnology* ナノテクノロジーの歴史

41

Practice 4 **Do you think nanotechnology will help save our future life?**

ナノテクノロジーは救世主ですか？

1. Two scientists have contributed to the development of nanotechnology. Richard Feynman, an American **physicist**《物理学者》, first introduced the idea of manipulating atoms and molecules in 1959. Norio Taniguchi, a Japanese researcher at the Tokyo University of Science, invented the term 'nanotechnology' in 1974.

2. The field of nanotechnology has been expanding since the 1980s, when scientists began studying materials at the **nanoscale**《ナノスケールの》 level. Nanotechnology research has led to continuous improvements in the commercial production of **semiconductors**《半導体》. Semiconductors have created the computer revolution. Useful **applications**《応用》 of nanotechnology now exist in many fields such as medicine and AI.

3. Nanotechnology processes separate, unify, or **deform**《変形する》 materials **one atom or molecule at a time**《原子や分子を一つずつ》. These processes involve working at scales of 100 **nanometers**《ナノメーター》 and below. A human hair is about 50,000 to 100,000 nanometers wide, while **a strand of DNA**《一本鎖のDNA(核酸)》 is 2.5 nanometers wide.

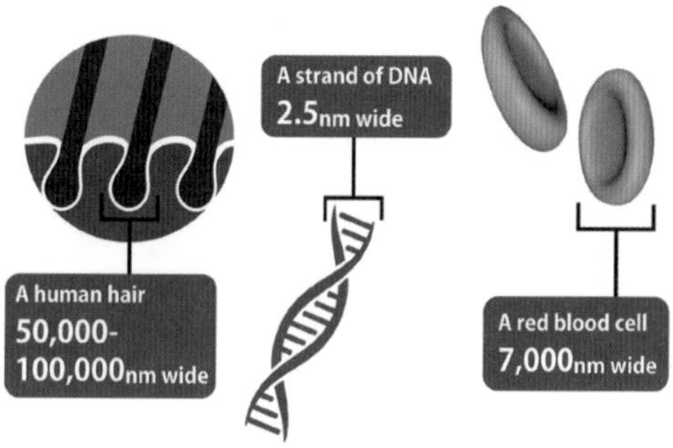

4. Objects at the nanoscale level act differently from those in daily life. For example, ordinary objects are affected by gravity. If your pencil rolls off the desk, it will fall to the floor. However, the **mass**《質量》 of nanoscale objects is so small that **gravitational force**《重力》 has little effect. In other words, gravitational force is extremely weak between **nanosized particles**《ナノサイズの粒子》.

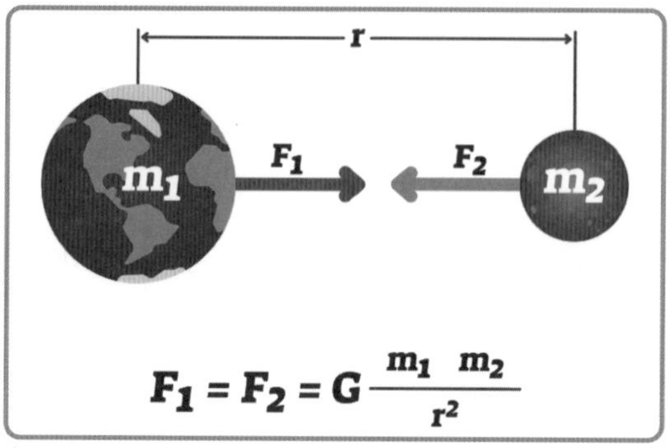

4. *Text summarization* *How to make a summary* 必要な情報のまとめ方

Practice 5 **Summary of Topic 1 Recite it** Topic 1（前ページ）のまとめ　暗唱しよう

1. Two scientists have contributed to the development of nanotechnology.
2. The field of nanotechnology has been expanding since the 1980s.
3. Nanotechnology processes separate, unify or deform materials one atom or molecule at a time.
4. Objects at the nanoscale level act differently than those in daily life.

Practice 6 **Read and summarize** 読んで内容を把握してサマリーを作成しよう 42

Richard Feynman was born in New York City in 1918. He studied physics at the Massachusetts Institute of Technology and received his **doctorate**《博士号》 at Princeton University in 1942. Now Feynman is regarded as the 'father of nanotechnology.'

During World War II, he was recruited to serve as a staff member of the U.S. atomic bomb project at Princeton University. He then observed the first explosion of an atomic bomb on July 16, 1945 and later felt anxiety about the force.

At the end of the war, Feynman became associate professor at Cornell University. In 1950 he became professor of **theoretical physics**《理論物理学》 at the California Institute of Technology. In a 1959 lecture at Caltech, he spoke about "the room at the bottom" between micrometer magnitudes and the magnitudes of atoms and molecules. That encouraged a lot of researchers to make their instruments and methods smaller and smaller.

Feynman developed an approach to **quantum electrodynamics**《量子電磁力学》 **(QED)**. That changed the way we understand the nature of waves and particles. He was awarded the Nobel Prize for Physics in 1965, along with the other winners of the Nobel Prize, Julian S. Schwinger and Shinichiro Tomonaga.

In 1968, he invented a theory of **partons**《パートン模型》, or **hypothetical**《仮説の》 hard particles inside the **nucleus of the atom**《原子の核》. It helps lead to the modern understanding of **quarks**《クォーク:素粒子の一つ》. He died in 1988.

Complete the summary 適切な語（句）を入れてサマリーを完成しよう

Richard Feynman, known as the '(　　　　　) of nanotechnology,' served as a staff member of the U.S. (　　　　　　　) bomb project. He was professor of (　　　　　　) physics at the California Institute of Technology and won the Nobel Prize. He invented a theory of (　　　　　), or hypothetical hard (　　　　　　) inside the nucleus of the atom.

Research **What are you interested in when reading this passage? Choose one and do research.**

5. *Topic 2* *Nanofabrication techniques* ナノ加工技術

43

Practice 7 **There are two main approaches to nanofabrication. Do you think they will greatly change our life style in the future?**

ナノ加工技術は未来の生活様式を変えるか？

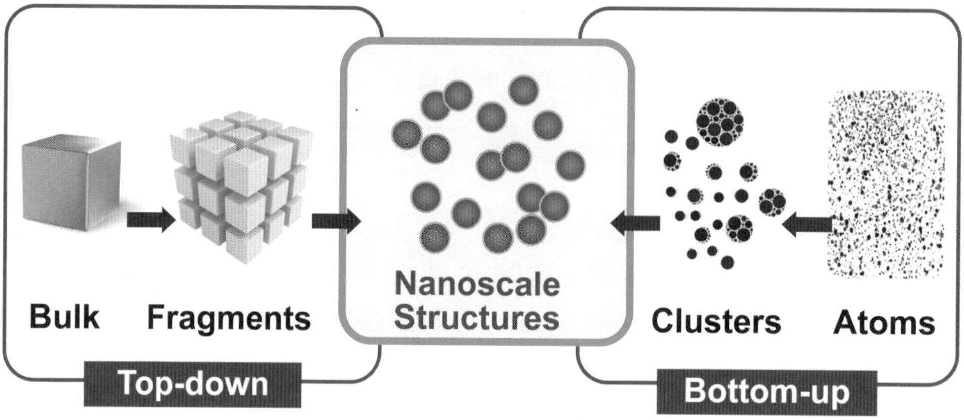

During the last 20 years, we have seen the development and **advancement**《進歩》 of various nanofabrication techniques. Such techniques can be divided into two categories: top-down and bottom-up approaches. Top-down nanofabrication involves cutting away unwanted material. It is similar to the process of carving something from a block of wood. Bottom-up nanofabrication is a **synthesis**《合成》 approach that involves putting pieces together. It is similar to building a house one brick at a time.

The goal of nanofabrication is to create commercial products. To be successful, a process technique must be flexible, reliable, scalable, and cost effective.

Top-down approaches have worked well: **optical lithography**《光リソグラフィ》 and **nanoimprint**《ナノインプリント》 **lithography**《リソグラフィー》. Optical lithography is well-known as the standard way in which computer chips are made. Nanoimprint lithography is a less expensive technique used for fabricating nanometer scale patterns. It has wide applications outside the high-tech computer world.

Bottom-up approaches experience many technological challenges, including the ability to place pieces in the correct positions. These challenges affect the **flexibility**《柔軟性》 and **reliability**《信頼性》 of production. As **ongoing**《進行中の》 research helps overcome such challenges, bottom-up approaches may become more widely used in the future.

6. *Understanding nanotechnology Key terms* ナノテクノロジーを考えるのに必要な用語

Practice 8 **Discuss the key terms on nanotechnology: nanotechnology, carbon nanotubes: (CNTs), and nanocomputers.**

Nanotechnology

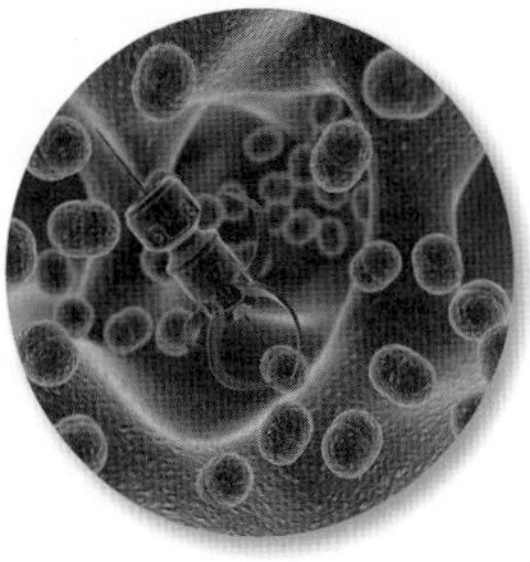

Nanotechnology has the potential to change the world. It will help clean the environment, solve major health problems, and increase the **efficiency**《効率》 of **energy consumption**《エネルギー消費》. Nanotechnology **advocates**《支持者》 claim that future products will be more functional, smaller, cheaper, and lighter, requiring less energy and fewer raw materials to manufacture. All of these will be possible through continued advancements in nanotechnology.

Carbon nanotubes: (CNTs)

Carbon nanotubes (CNTs) are **graphene sheets**《グラフェン：結合炭素原子シート》 rolled into a **cylindrical shape**《円筒形》, possessing unique structural and **electrical properties**《電気特性》 that make them ideal for a wide variety of applications. They come in single-walled (SWNTs), double-walled (DWNTs) and multi-walled (MWNTs) varieties.

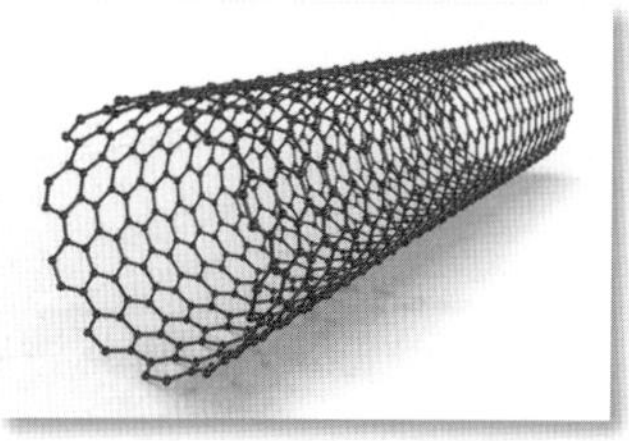

Nanocomputers

A nanocomputer is a computer whose fundamental components are only a few nanometers (<100nm) in size. There are electronic, **biochemical**《生物化学的》, organic, and **quantum**《量子》 nanocomputers, and some are so small that they can only be seen through a microscope. Nanocomputing is part of the emerging field of nanotechnology, which deals with materials at a molecular level.

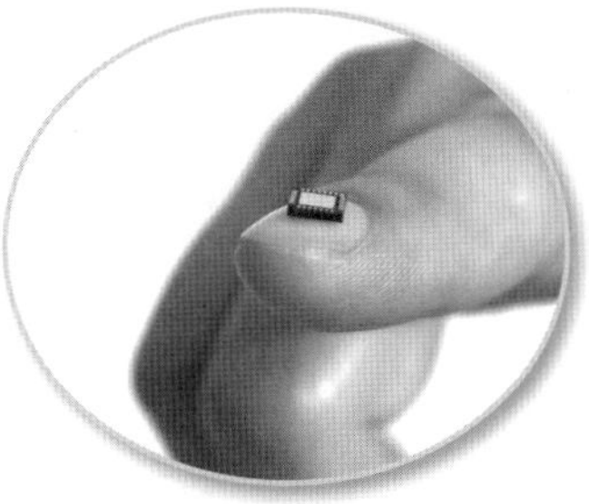

7. *Learning outcomes What have you learned?* 学んだことの整理

Self-assessment 自己評価をしよう

I can listen to and read **what nanotechnology is**.	0---30---50---70---100%
I can speak and write about **how nanotechnology changes our life**.	0---30---50---70---100%
I can understand **the ideas and problems about nanotechnology**.	0---30---50---70---100%

Practice 9 A summary of learning: write a summary of what you have learned in this unit.

Key terms

Key sentences

Key facts

Your understanding

Your thoughts

Unit 9

The hydrogen fuel cell train

未来に向けて走る水素燃料電池列車

1. *CLIL attainment target*　この課の学習目標を確認しよう

1. I can listen to and read **what hydrogen fuel cell trains are.**　聞く・読む技能
2. I can speak and write about **how hydrogen fuel cell trains work.**　話す・書く技能
3. I can understand **the ideas and problems about hydrogen fuel cell trains.**　関連の内容の理解

2. *Introduction　What is the hydrogen fuel cell train?*　水素燃料電池列車とは何か？

Practice 1 Listen and check your understanding　聞き取ってみよう　44

1) Where was the first hydrogen fuel cell train introduced?

a) Japan　b) the U.S.　c) Germany

2) What are the by-products of a hydrogen fuell celll?

a) water and heat　b) water and air　c) air and heat

Practice 2 Read and check your understanding　情報を理解しよう　45

Hydrogen is expected to become an important new source of energy in the future. When hydrogen and oxygen are combined under certain conditions, they react in a way that **generates**《生成する》 water and electricity. Hydrogen fuel cells are **generators**《発電機》 designed to capture the power of that reaction and convert it into a form that can be used by trains and other vehicles. In Japan, more than 30% of trains still currently use fossil fuels. These trains must be replaced with those that use only clean energy such as hydrogen fuel cells. In the future, it is expected that all rail transportation around the world will use clean energy that generates only water **emissions**《排出》.

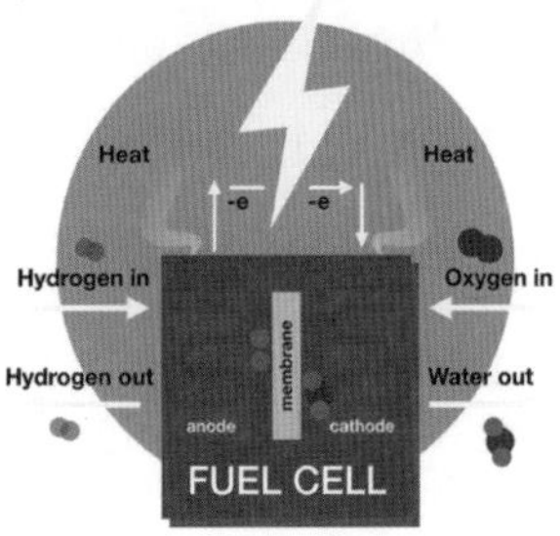

Practice 3 Talk in pairs　内容を確認して、英語でおしゃべりしよう

What do you think about hydrogen fuel cell trains?

e.g.　A: Do you want to take a hydrogen fuel cell train? You can take that train in Germany.
B: Yeah, how about you?
A: Of course, I would like to take a hydrogen fuel cell train.

3. *Topic 1* *Hydrogen fuel cells vs. diesel engines* 水素燃料電池 VS ディーゼルエンジン

Practice 4 **What advantages or disadvantages do hydrogen fuel cells have?** 46
燃料電池列車とディーゼルエンジン列車の違いは何でしょうか？

1. Railway **electrification**《電化》 is not available in many countries. On lightly travelled routes across large distances, for instance, it may not be economically **feasible**《実現可能な》 to install the necessary infrastructure. Also, extreme weather conditions in some areas may increase the risk of power interruptions.

2. Power plants must provide a consistent supply of electricity to keep electric trains running. In some areas, it is not easy to obtain electricity, especially from renewable sources, such as **geothermal**《地熱》 and **hydroelectric**《水力発電の》 power plants. Even in Japan, where almost 70% of trains are electric, this requirement can be hard to fulfill.

3. Diesel engines produce **exhaust gases**《排気ガス》 such as CO_2, CO, and NOx, although they generate strong **torque**《トルク》. Freight trains and ships often use diesel engines, which were once thought to be environmentally friendly. Now, many people **think otherwise**《そうは考えない》.

4. We now know that diesel engines pollute the environment. Some research shows that diesel engines produce more pollution than gasoline engines. Also, diesel engines are big contributors to global warming and acid rain. So, more eco-friendly options are needed.

5. Hydrogen fuel cells generate electricity with a **chemical reaction**《化学反応》 of oxygen and hydrogen. Oxygen is easy to obtain from the air, but hydrogen is not. When oxygen **combines with**《化合する》 hydrogen in a **redox reaction**《レドックス(酸化還元)反応》, electricity and water is produced. Hydrogen fuel cells do not generate pollutants of any kind.

6. The world's first hydrogen fuel cell train began service in Germany in 2018. The train, called the **Coradia iLint**《コラディア・アイリント》, can carry 300 passengers at speeds up to 140km/h over its 124km route between **Buxtehude**《ブクステフーデ》 and **Cuxhaven**《ククスハーフェン》 in northern Germany.

4. *Text summarization How to make a summary* 必要な情報のまとめ方

Practice 5 **Summary of Topic 1 Recite it** Topic 1 (前ページ) のまとめ 暗唱しよう

1. Railway electrification is not available in many countries.
2. Power plants must provide a consistent supply of electricity to keep electric trains running.
3. Diesel engines produce exhaust gases such as CO2, CO, and NOx.
4. We now know that diesel engines pollute the environment.
5. Hydrogen fuel cells generate electricity with a chemical reaction of oxygen and hydrogen.
6. The world's first hydrogen fuel cell train began service in Germany in 2018.

Practice 6 **Read and summarize** 読んで内容を把握してサマリーを作成しよう 47

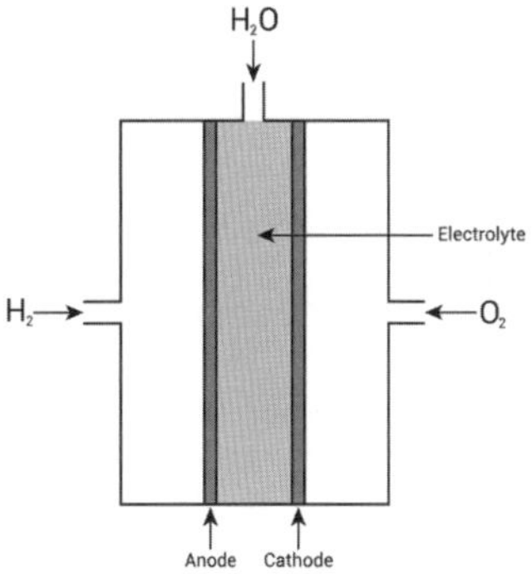

Polymer electrolyte fuel cells《固体高分子形燃料電池》 **(PEFCs)** are most commonly used in hydrogen fuel cell trains. PEFCs are suitable due to their **low-temperature operation**《低温運転》, high **power density**《電力密度》, and high **energy conversion efficiency**《エネルギー交換効率》.

Hydrogen fuel cells generate electricity by first separating protons and electrons within hydrogen atoms. Then, while protons move to the **cathode**《カソード》 side of the fuel cell, electrons flow through an external circuit to create an output current. At the cathode side, the protons react with oxygen **molecules**《分子》 and electrons to produce water.

PEFCs can operate at temperatures below 100˚C, so they are suitable for use in transport applications. Despite their advantages, PEFCs still have some technical challenges. These include water management in **electrolyte membranes**《電解質膜》 and reduction of platinum **catalysts**《触媒》.

PEFCs are the key technology behind new emission-free hydrogen fuel cell trains. They are safer for the environment and human health than diesel trains. These new trains can also attain speeds of up to 140km/h. Their performance is therefore comparable to conventional trains.

Complete the summary 適切な語を入れてサマリーを完成しよう

PEFCs are most commonly used in (   ) fuel cell trains. Hydrogen fuel cells generate (   ) by separating protons and electrons within hydrogen atoms. PEFCs can operate at (   ) below 100˚C. PEFCs are the key technology behind new (   ) hydrogen fuel cell trains.

Research **What are you interested in when reading this passage? Choose one and do research.**

5. Topic 2 Hydrogen energy society 水素エネルギー社会

48

Practice 7 **Making good use of hydrogen energy can help sustain the environment. What do we need to better utilize new sources of energy, like hydrogen fuels cells?**

水素エネルギー利用のために必要なことは何か？

Hydrogen fuel cells use oxygen and hydrogen to generate electricity. Unlike batteries that lose power over time, hydrogen fuel cells continue to produce energy as long as the fuel source is available.

Oxygen can be obtained easily from air, but hydrogen is not available in large quantities naturally on Earth. Most hydrogen is produced from fossil fuels now. Several production processes exist, but the cheapest and most commonly used process is **steam reforming**《水蒸気改質》. This method produces hydrogen from natural gas.

In the steam reforming process, hydrogen is obtained from natural gas, which mainly consists of methane (CH_4). The process involves heating the natural gas to a high temperature in the presence of steam and a nickel catalyst. The resulting reaction breaks up the methane molecules and forms hydrogen. Unfortunately, CO, CO_2, and other greenhouse gases are also produced.

Electrolysis《電解》 is an alternative method of producing hydrogen. This method uses electricity to split water molecules (H_2O) into hydrogen and oxygen. Electrolysis is potentially a cleaner and more sustainable way to produce hydrogen.

There are other challenges associated with hydrogen. For example, since hydrogen has a low energy **density**《密度》, it needs to be stored and transported under high pressure. Moreover, hydrogen is highly flammable, so great care must be taken in its production, storage and transportation.

Reducing CO_2 emissions is urgently needed to counteract the effects of global warming. Hydrogen fuel cells can produce energy with no emissions, so they are a necessary source of power, even if hydrogen is still difficult to obtain.

6. *Understanding the hydrogen fuel cell train Key terms*

水素燃料電池列車を考えるのに必要な用語

Practice 8 **Discuss the key terms on the hydrogen fuel cell train: hydrogen fuel cells, fuel cell vehicles (FCVs), and the Coradia iLint.**

Hydrogen fuel cells

Hydrogen fuel cells are devices that generate electricity by a chemical reaction. The fuel cell has two **electrodes**《電極》 – an anode and a cathode – and an electrolyte membrane. Hydrogen fuel is supplied to the anode while oxygen is supplied to the cathode. At the anode, electrons are stripped from the hydrogen atoms and passed through an external circuit to the cathode, thereby producing an electric current. Protons pass through the electrolyte membrane to the cathode, where they join the electrons and oxygen to form water.

Fuel cell vehicles (FCVs)

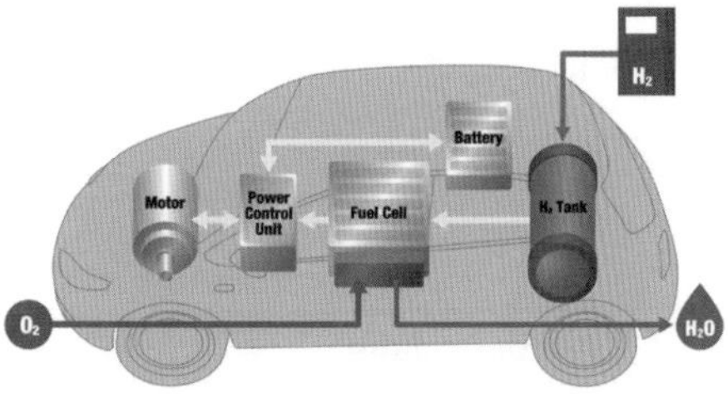

FCVs can support the transportation needs of modern societies while lowering their overall dependence on fossil fuels. By using hydrogen fuel cells that have no CO_2 emissions, FCVs don't create greenhouse gases which contribute to global warming. Of course, there are challenges to overcome, but the potential benefits are **substantial**《重要な》. Currently, FCVs are expensive and hydrogen fueling stations are not yet widely available.

The Coradia iLint

The Coradia iLint is the world's first passenger train that is powered exclusively by hydrogen fuel cells. This zero-emission train is silent and emits only steam and condensed water.

It is special for its combination of innovative elements: clean energy conversion, flexible energy storage in batteries, and smart management of electrical power for **traction**《トランクション:牽引力》 and onboard systems.

7. *Learning outcomes What have you learned?* 学んだことの整理

Self-assessment 自己評価をしよう

I can listen to and read **what hydrogen fuel cell trains are.**	0---30---50---70---100%
I can speak and write about **how hydrogen fuel cell trains work.**	0---30---50---70---100%
I can understand **the ideas and problems about hydrogen fuel cell trains.**	0---30---50---70---100%

Practice 9 **A summary of learning: write a summary of what you have learned in this unit.**

Key terms

Key sentences

Key facts

Your understanding

Your thoughts

Technology column 3: Some issues of IoT

49

Discuss what you learned about it and what you want to know about it.

According to a study by International Data Corporation (IDC), which offers **expertise**《専門知識》 on technology and industry opportunities and trends in many countries, there will be 41.6 billion IoT (Internet of Things) devices in 2025. IDC estimates that they will be capable of generating 79.4 zettabytes (ZB) of data.

1ZB = 1 000 000 000 000 000 000 000 bytes

There are several critical issues relating to the use of IoT devices. Among these are the growing **sophistication**《精巧》 of cameras and sensors and the security of communications. With regard to the sophistication of sensors, IoT devices are usually designed to operate automatically and require more delicate movements: e.g. the operation of robot vacuum cleaners and air conditioners. The **adjustments**《調整》 that humans **unconsciously**《無意識に》 make need to be **optimized**《最適化する》 on the software side through technologies such as machine learning. However, even when the software is perfect, the hardware must be capable of performing the operation.

IoT devices are designed to record human life in order to enrich it. This involves the collection and storage of large amounts of personal information, such as what you ordered online and the time you leave and arrive back home each day. Such data must be recorded and stored securely in order to maintain a high level of privacy. This is especially true for data that are collected through hardware, processed in software, and then sent to cloud servers through communication networks. In these situations, a high degree of privacy protection is required.

IoT devices must protect the privacy of personal information that they collect and store. Also, they must have adequate safety features to ensure that they do not physically harm humans. The **integration**《統合》 of these two factors is a **dilemma**《ジレンマ》 for the development of IoT devices. Modern engineers are now expected to have both the technical aspect of enriching our lives and the human care aspect of using IOT devices safely.

Paragraph writing about Technology column 3

What did you learn about this topic?

What do you want to know more about this topic?

Unit 10

Protein: research expands to outer space

宇宙で発展するタンパク質研究

1. *CLIL attainment target*　この課の学習目標を確認しよう

1. I can listen to and read **what protein research is.**　聞く・読む技能
2. I can speak and write **how protein research works.**　話す・書く技能
3. I can understand **the ideas and problems about protein research.**　関連の内容の理解

2. *Introduction*　*What is protein?*　タンパク質とは何か？

Practice 1　**Listen and check your understanding**　聞き取ってみよう　50

1) Takashi needs a good diet to be a good rugby player. What did Jane advise him to eat?

a) beans　　b) fish　　c) meat

2) What did Jane and Takashi mainly talk about?

a) weight training　　b) protein to help build muscle　　c) eating steak

Practice 2　**Read and check your understanding**　情報を理解しよう　51

Human bodies are made up of organs, such as the brain, heart, lungs, eyes, skin, and muscles. Each organ performs specific functions and is composed of **tissues**《組織》 that contain various cells. Each cell has thousands of proteins, which are composed of **amino acids**《アミノ酸》 linked together by **peptide bonds**《ペプチド結合》 to form **polypeptide chains**《ポリペプチド鎖》. Proteins carry out a vast array of functions and can take on many complex shapes. Despite their differences, however, proteins work together in a coordinated way to support every biochemical reaction that occurs in living things.

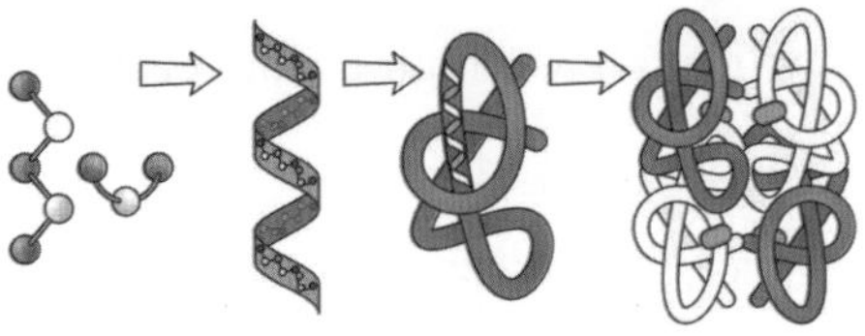

Structure of Proteins

Practice 3　**Talk in pairs**　内容を確認して、英語でおしゃべりしよう

What kind of food has protein?

e.g.　A: Do you know what kind of food has protein?
B: Yes. Natto and milk have lots of proteins. They are part of my daily diet.
A: That's good.

3. *Topic 1* Protein research in outer space 宇宙におけるタンパク質研究

52

Practice 4 **Why is protein research conducted in outer space?**

タンパク質研究が宇宙で行われていることを知っていますか？ なぜ宇宙で行われていると思いますか？

1. Protein is an essential component of all cells, so researchers are interested in learning more about its structure and function. However, since protein molecules are too small to be seen and handled directly, they must be arranged into crystals before being studied.

2. Researchers study **protein crystals**《タンパク質結晶》 using a technique called **X-ray crystallography**《X線結晶構造解析》 **(XRC)**. It involves **irradiating**《照射する》 the crystals with X-rays and then carefully observing how the X-rays are reflected.

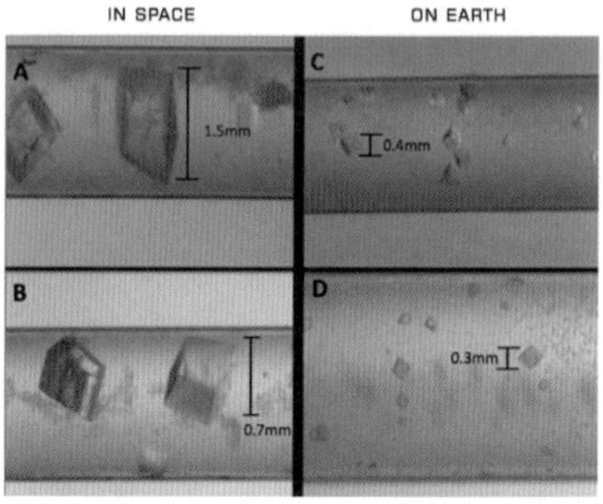

3. Researchers need high quality protein crystals to conduct effective experiments. They can reveal protein structures in detail, but how can you grow such high quality crystals?

4. Some research on protein crystals is now being conducted at the International Space Station (ISS). Doing protein research at a space station is advantageous, because it is easier to grow high quality crystals in low gravity environments.

5. Protein crystals grown in space are of much higher quality than those grown on Earth. The difference in quality relates to the fact that there is no **convection**《対流》 from density differences in **microgravity**《微小重力》. Space can therefore serve as a very stable environment in which to grow high quality crystals.

6. Researchers are now able to better understand the structure of proteins, thanks to successful research in space. Protein research in space will aid the development of new medicines and materials, so it has the potential to affect our life in many positive ways.

4. *Text summarization How to make a summary* 必要な情報のまとめ方

Practice 5 **Summary of Topic 1 Recite it** Topic 1（前ページ）のまとめ 暗唱しよう

1.	Protein is an essential component of all cells.
2.	Researchers study protein crystals using a technique called X-ray crystallography.
3.	Researchers need high quality protein crystals to conduct effective experiments.
4.	Some research on protein crystals is now being conducted at the ISS.
5.	Protein crystals grown in space are of much higher quality than those grown on Earth.
6.	Researchers are now able to better understand the structure of proteins.

Practice 6 **Read and summarize** 読んで内容を把握してサマリーを作成しよう 53

The relationship between protein and disease is not always clearly understood. That is because the human body contains many proteins that can be impacted by disease.

Research has been conducted to explore the relationship between protein and disease. However, such research relies on being able to understand the structure and function of proteins.

Some researchers use microgravity protein **crystallization**《結晶化》 for studying protein structures. Protein crystallization is a process of growing protein crystals for research purposes. Growing the crystals in a microgravity environment is preferable, because it produces relatively large crystals with fewer impurities and defects. NASA has carried out such experiments on board space shuttle missions for years.

High quality protein crystals grown in space are returned to Earth for further study. Researchers can better understand the structure and function of proteins, as they obtain detailed information from space-grown crystals. This has led to the development of new, effective medicines for the treatment of diseases.

Complete the summary 適切な語を入れてサマリーを完成しよう

The relationship between (　　　　　) and disease is not always clearly understood. Research has been conducted to (　　　　　) the relationship between protein and (　　　　　). Some researchers use (　　　　　) protein crystallization for studying protein structures. High quality protein (　　　　　) grown in space are returned to Earth for further study.

Research **What are you interested in when reading this passage? Choose one and do research.**

5. Topic 2　The JAXA Protein Crystal Growth (JAXA PCG) 54

JAXA 高品質タンパク質結晶生成実験

Practice 7 **Many research projects are in progress in the ISS. Protein research in outer space is useful for the development of new medicines. What do you want to do in a microgravity environment?** 宇宙環境を活かした実験が進んでいる。何ができるだろうか？

Protein research has entered a new stage. The Japan Aerospace Exploration Agency (JAXA) offers scientists opportunities to conduct a variety of microgravity research experiments in space.

Many projects are in progress at Japan's Kibo laboratory aboard the ISS. Each project conducts experiments that must be first designed and prepared by scientists on Earth. All necessary materials and equipment are then sent to the space station so that Japanese **astronauts**《宇宙飛行士》 can perform the actual experiments. One such project is called the JAXA Protein Crystal Growth (JAXA PCG).

Dr. Yasumitsu Sakamoto of Iwate Medical University became involved in the JAXA PCG project. "At first," he said, "I had no idea that my knowledge of **structural biology**《構造生物学》 could have any connection to space experiments. So, I was surprised that I could join this project." After the project team finally got better experimental results in 2016, he said, "I feel really happy about it."

Dr. Yasumitsu Sakamoto of Iwate Medical University
©JAXA

Space experiments play a critical role in supporting protein research. Also, the results of such research are leading to the development of new **antibacterial drugs**《抗菌薬》 and medicines for the treatment of **muscular dystrophy**《筋ジストロフィー》, **Alzheimer's disease**《アルツハイマー病》, and cancer.

Understanding the complex structure and function of proteins could help unlock the mysteries of life. It can also provide hints about what life is and what being alive means. For this reason, we should pay close attention to the exciting new advancements in protein research.

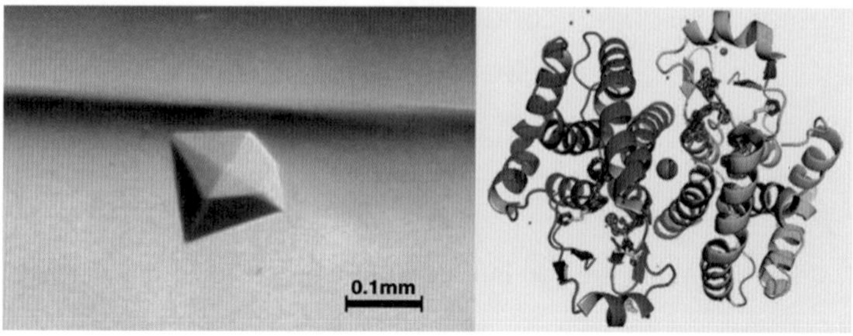

Crystal and structure of proteins involved in the progression of muscular dystroph
©JAXA

6. *Understanding Protein Research Key terms*

タンパク質研究を考えるのに必要な用語

Practice 8 **Discuss the key terms on protein research: amino acids, protein structure, and JAXA and the ISS.**

Amino acids

Amino acids are **organic molecules**《有機分子》 that living **organisms**《有機体》 use to make proteins. Carbon, hydrogen, oxygen, and **nitrogen**《窒素》 are the main elements in amino acids. The human body needs 20 different amino acids to grow and function properly. Eleven of these can be produced naturally by our bodies. However, the other nine can only be obtained through a healthy, well-balanced diet.

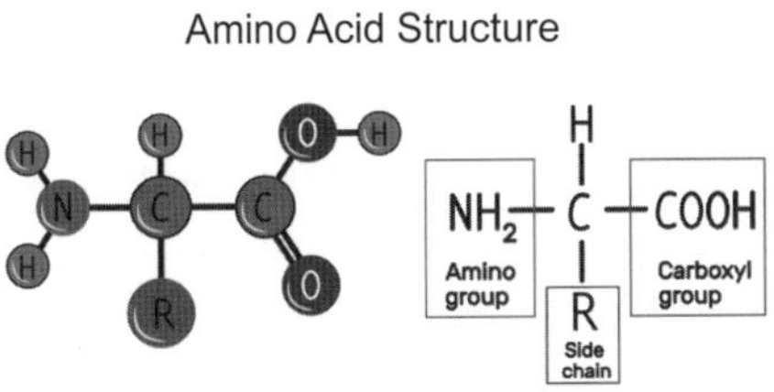

Protein structure

Proteins are long chains of amino acids that are joined together by **peptide bonds**《ペプチド結合》. These chains, which are also called **polypeptide chains**《ポリペプチド鎖》, can then fold, loop, and curve into unique **configurations**《立体構造》 depending upon interactions between **amino acid side chains**《アミノ酸側鎖》.

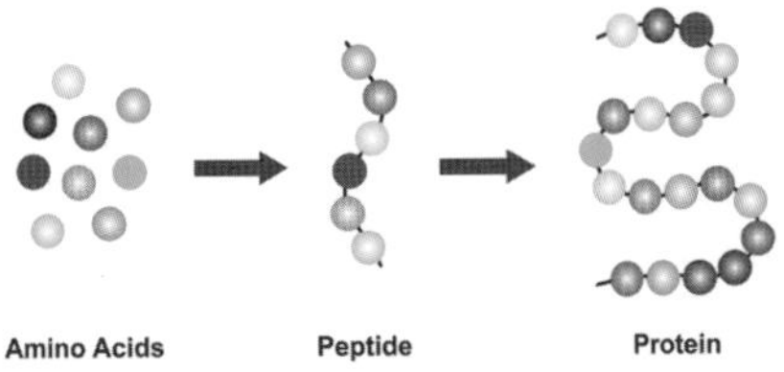

JAXA and the ISS

The JAXA is the Japanese national **aerospace**《宇宙空間》 and space agency. It is the **core performance agency**《中核的実施機関》 responsible for conducting all **integrated operations**《統合された運用》 relating to space, including research, technological development, and the launch of satellites and other spacecrafts. JAXA sometimes sends astronauts to conduct research at the ISS, which is a weightless laboratory orbiting 400km above the Earth at a speed of 28,800km/h. Astronauts on the ISS can experience 16 sunrises and sunsets each day, since it takes only about 90 minutes for the space station to make a complete revolution around the Earth.

7. Learning outcomes What have you learned? 学んだことの整理

Self-assessment 自己評価をしよう

I can listen to and read **what protein research is.**	0---30---50---70---100%
I can speak and write about **how protein research works.**	0---30---50---70---100%
I can understand **the ideas and problems about protein research.**	0---30---50---70---100%

Practice 9 **A summary of learning: write a summary of what you have learned in this unit.**

Key terms

Key sentences

Key facts

Your understanding

Your thoughts

Unit 11

Shifting to renewable energy

再生可能なエネルギーへ移行

1. *CLIL attainment target*　この課の学習目標を確認しよう

1. I can listen to and read **what renewable energy is.**　聞く・読む技能
2. I can speak and write about **how renewable energy works.**　話す・書く技能
3. I can understand **the ideas and problems about renewable energy**.　関連の内容の理解

2. *Introduction　What is renewable energy?*　再生可能エネルギーとは何か？

Practice 1　Listen and check your understanding　聞き取ってみよう　55

1) What is the most used source of energy in Japan?

a) coal　　b) oil　　c) liquefied natural gas (LNG)

2) What is the biggest advantage of using renewable energy?

a) economy　　b) safety　　c) sustainability

Practice 2　Read and check your understanding　情報を理解しよう　56

Renewable energy is created from resources such as sunshine, wind, and water. It is called clean or green power because it doesn't pollute the environment. Some scientists argue that not everything renewable is sustainable, while not everything sustainable is necessarily renewable. Renewable energy includes **solar power**《太陽光発電》 or **photovoltaics**, **hydroelectric power**《水力発電》, wind power, **geothermal power**《地熱発電》, and **biomass**《バイオマス》. The amount of **greenhouse gases**《温室効果ガス》 **emitted**《排出する》 by these renewable energy sources is much less than that of **fossil fuels**《化石燃料》 such as coal and oil.

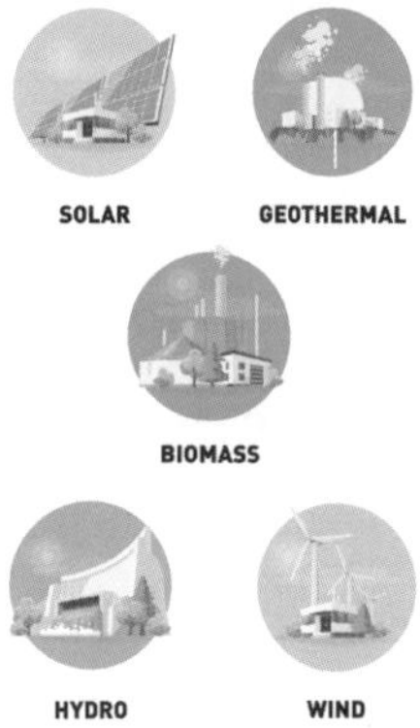

Practice 3　Talk in pairs　内容を確認して、英語でおしゃべりしよう

What type of energy do you use most?

e.g.　A: I don't know. I always use electricity.
B: It means you use fossil fuels, right?
A: I am not sure about the source of energy. I need to check it.

3. *Topic 1 Solar power as renewable energy* 再生可能エネルギーとしての太陽光発電

Practice 4 What are the characteristics of renewable energy? 57
再生可能エネルギーの特徴は何でしょうか？

1. Many machines in our daily life are powered by electricity. Without electricity, they will not run well. Being unable to run a household appliance may be inconvenient, and being unable to run a medical device may be life-threatening. A lot of electricity can be generated from the burning of fossil fuels.
2. Fossil fuels emit greenhouse gases when burned and a greenhouse effect occurs. This effect leads to environmental problems, particularly **global warming**《地球温暖化》 and **climate**《気候》 **change**《変動》. So we need clean and renewable energy.
3. Solar power is energy which is **converted**《変換する》 into **thermal**《熱の》 or electrical energy. It is the cleanest and most **abundant**《豊富な》 renewable energy source available.
4. **Solar panels**《太陽電池パネル》 are also called **photovoltaic (PV) panels**《太陽光(PV)パネル》. These panels contain solar cells that can absorb light energy and emit electrical energy. This is called the **photovoltaic effect**《光起電力効果》.
5. A solar cell contains everything that needs to transform sunlight into clean electricity. It uses semi-conducting materials that can produce a flow of electrons from solar energy. This results in direct current that is then transferred over wires.
6. Solar power technology has rapidly advanced, but advantages and disadvantages still exist. In terms of the advantages, solar power doesn't use fossil fuels, emit greenhouse gases, or produce noise or vibration when generating electricity. On the other hand, the biggest disadvantage is that the amount of power generated over a specific period of time will depend upon the amount of sunlight available. To put it simply, solar panels are unable to produce electricity without sunlight.

7. Solar power helps reduce our **carbon footprint**《カーボンフットプリント》, which is good for the environment. Also, powering home appliances with electricity obtained from roof-mounted solar panels is very convenient. As a free source of renewable energy, the sun provides us with more energy than we could ever use.

4. *Text summarization How to make a summary* 必要な情報のまとめ方

Practice 5 **Summary of Topic 1 Recite it** Topic 1（前ページ）のまとめ 暗唱しよう

1. Many machines in our daily life are powered by electricity.
2. Fossil fuels emit greenhouse gases when burned.
3. Solar power is energy which is converted into thermal or electrical energy.
4. Solar panels are also called photovoltaic (PV) panels.
5. A solar cell contains everything that needs to transform sunlight into clean electricity.
6. Solar power technology has rapidly advanced, but advantages and disadvantages still exist.
7. Solar power helps reduce our carbon footprint, which is good for the environment.

Practice 6 **Read and summarize** 読んで内容を把握してサマリーを作成しよう 58

These days the weather seems strange. Many people now worry about global warming. We will examine reasons why global warming is occurring and discuss some possible solutions.

Global warming is mainly the result of CO_2 emissions and **deforestation**《森林伐採》. Power plants burn fossil fuels, which emit CO_2 into the atmosphere. The burning of **transportation fuels**《輸送用燃料》 also generates CO_2 emissions. Deforestation contributes to global warming by reducing the number of trees and plants that can absorb CO_2 from the atmosphere. As a result, more CO_2 remains there.

There are ways to solve the problems associated with global warming or reduce the effects. Governments need to take action to help people reduce their **dependence**《依存》 on fossil fuels. Also, people can help by changing their lifestyles. They can stop using cars that rely on gasoline, or they can **patronize**《ひいきする》 companies that use renewable energy. Even small things such as conserving electricity at home can help.

Global warming is a phenomenon that affects all of us in the form of rising sea levels, **extreme weather**《異常気象》, and natural disasters. Governments and people must strive to reduce the causes and effects of global warming.

Complete the summary 適切な語を入れてサマリーを完成しよう

Global warming is mainly the result of CO_2 (　　　　　) and deforestation. There are ways to solve the problems associated with global warming or reduce the (　　　　　). Since global warming is a (　　　　　) that affects all of us in the form of rising sea levels, extreme weather, and natural disasters.

Research **What are you interested in when reading this passage? Choose one and do research.**

5. Topic 2 Renewable and non-renewable energy 59

再生可能エネルギーと再生不能エネルギー

Practice 7 **How do you use energy resources? How do you stop using fossil fuels? Discuss how renewable and non-renewable energy should be used.**

化石燃料など再生不可能エネルギーと再生可能エネルギーはどのように使われているでしょうか？

There are two types of energy: renewable and non-renewable energy. Renewable energy comes from resources that are abundantly available or can be refilled easily. Non-renewable energy comes from resources that are limited in supply and will eventually be exhausted, if used widely. Both types of energy have advantages and disadvantages.

Renewable energy is generated from natural processes and phenomena, so its strength and availability may vary over time. As a result, electric power derived from such sources may not always be available. This could be a disadvantage in some situations.

Most non-renewable energy sources are fossil fuels such as LNG, coal, and oil. In 2011, fossil fuels powered 83% of the world's energy needs. However, fossil fuels are in limited supply and are not easily **replenished**《補充される》, so eventually they may be used up. Also, since fossil fuels store large amounts of carbon, burning them adds carbon dioxide to the atmosphere. That contributes to global warming and climate change.

Nuclear power can reduce greenhouse gas emissions, but the production of nuclear power involves other risks. All Japanese people know about the terrible situation that occurred at the Fukushima Daichi nuclear power plant following the large earthquake and tsunami in Tohoku on March 11th, 2011. Efforts to **decontaminate**《除染する》 that site and the surrounding area have required many years.

We need to discuss whether to choose renewable or non-renewable energy. It is still difficult to completely shift from non-renewable energy to renewable energy. However, we will have to reduce CO_2 emissions to stop climate change. When thinking about energy choices now and in the future, we must focus on the issue of **sustainability**《持続可能性》 as well.

6. *Understanding renewable energy Key terms*

再生可能で持続可能なエネルギーへ移行を考えるのに必要な用語

Practice 8 **Discuss the key terms on renewable energy: electricity generation, biomass, and renewable energy use.**

Electricity generation

An **electric generator**《発電機》 is a device that converts **motive power**《原動力》 (mechanical energy) into electrical power. Its design typically uses **coils of insulated wire**《絶縁導線コイル》 wrapped around a **stationary cylinder**《固定シリンダー》 that is attached to a rotating **electromagnetic**《電磁気の》 shaft. As the shaft rotates, a small electrical current is induced within each section of the wire coil. These **localized**《局所的な》 currents combine to form one large current, which then travels from the generator to end users through power lines.

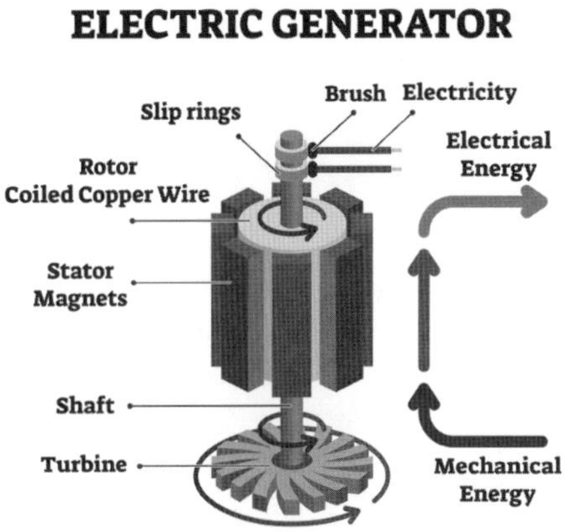

Biomass

Biomass refers to all kinds of **organic waste compounds**《有機廃棄物化合物》 such as food and agricultural waste. Some types of biomass are burned as fuels to operate **steam turbine generators**《蒸気タービン発電機》, while others are used to make transportation fuels such as **ethanol**《エタノール》. Although biomass typically releases CO_2 when burned, it is still classified as a renewable energy source since **photosynthesis**《光合成》 enables the carbon to be re-absorbed by other plants in their growth cycle.

Renewable energy use

There are several ways to power your home with renewable energy: **rooftop**《屋上の》 solar panels, wind turbines, and **hydro power**《水力発電》. They may help reduce or eliminate your **utility bills**《光熱費》. Also, using renewable energy may entitle you to certain **tax incentives**《税制上の優遇措置》, which are sometimes offered by the national, prefectural, or local government. This may also lead to additional cost savings.

7. Learning outcomes What have you learned? 学んだことの整理

Self-assessment 自己評価をしよう

I can listen to and read **what renewable energy is.**	0---30---50---70---100%
I can speak and write about **how renewable energy works.**	0---30---50---70---100%
I can understand **the ideas and problems about renewable energy.**	0---30---50---70---100%

Practice 9 **A summary of learning: write a summary of what you have learned in this unit.**

Key terms

Key sentences

Key facts

Your understanding

Your thoughts

Unit 12

Nature learning: engineers look to the natural world

エンジニアは自然界を見る

1. *CLIL attainment target*　この課の学習目標を確認しよう

1. I can listen to and read **what nature learning is.**　聞く・読む技能
2. I can speak and write about **how nature learning works.**　話す・書く技能
3. I can understand **the ideas and problems about nature learning.**　関連の内容の理解

2. *Introduction　What is nature learning?*　自然学習とは何か？

Practice 1　Listen and check your understanding　聞き取ってみよう　60

1) What is Kevin doing?

a) jogging　　b) drinking water　　c) walking on hands

2) What does Jane talk about to Kevin?

a) a giraffe's body mecanism　　b) how to drink water
c) walking on hands

Practice 2　Read and check your understanding　情報を理解しよう　61

What is the tallest animal on Earth? It is the giraffe. On average, adult giraffes are about 5 meters tall and have necks that are about 2 meters long. They are large graceful animals with unusual proportions. But have you ever wondered how giraffes' shapes affect their bodily functions? For example, how do they breathe with such long necks? How do their bodies regulate changes in **blood pressure**《血圧》 when they stand upright or bend down to drink? It turns out that giraffes have some special body mechanisms. In fact, these mechanisms are so special that scientists and engineers study them. As you learn more about giraffes, you may be amazed.

Practice 3　Talk in pairs　内容を確認して、英語でおしゃべりしよう

What animals do you like? What have you learned from them?

e.g.　A: I like giraffes. I have learned a lot from them.
　　B: I like cats. I'd like to live like them.
　　A: I would like to have a giraffe, but it's impossible.

3. *Topic 1 Unique aspects of giraffes* キリンってすごい

Practice 4 Do you know animals have some great mechanisms for survival? 62

動物は生存のためすばらしい仕組みを持っているのを知っていますか？

1. The giraffe's anatomy is unique, because it needs some special mechanisms to support its survival. Researchers are now studying these mechanisms to better understand how they operate.
2. A giraffe has a lung capacity that is about eight times greater than that of the average human. This enormous lung capacity is needed to compensate for the large volume of dead air, which is always present in the giraffe's long neck. Without such a large lung capacity, the giraffe would simply **inhale**《吸い込む》 and exhale the same air in its neck again and again.
3. A giraffe's heart is the biggest of all land **mammals**《哺乳類》. With an average weight of 12 kilograms, the heart has thick muscles that pump blood up the giraffe's long neck to its brain. As a result, giraffes have a blood pressure that is about twice that of other animals.
4. Due to its high blood pressure, a giraffe has a special mechanism called a '**wonder net**《奇驚網》,' which helps regulate blood flow to its brain. This spongy **tissue**《組織》 is filled with small **blood vessels**《血管》. It prevents a rush of blood from the **carotid artery**《頸(けい)動脈》 to the brain whenever the giraffe lowers its head to drink.

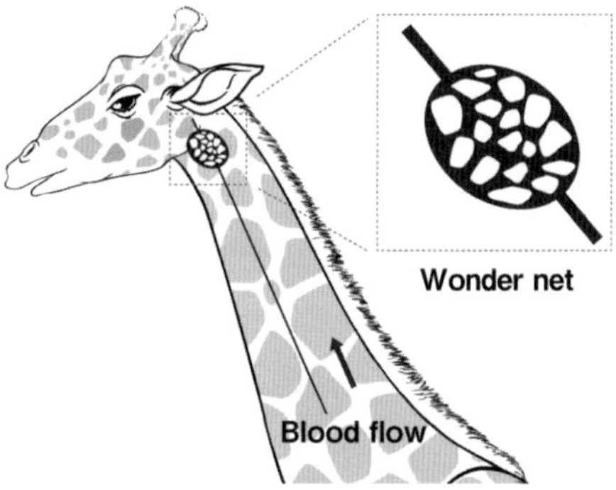

5. A series of valves in a giraffe's **jugular vein**《頸静脈》 also regulate blood flow. It returns blood from the head through the neck to the heart. Whenever the head is lowered, these one-way valves immediately close, thus preventing a reversal of blood flow to the brain.
6. The giraffe's unique physical characteristics have inspired researchers and engineers. It is difficult to find facts about wild giraffes, but researchers and engineers attempt to get data on them, doing experiments on them in laboratory and observing them by putting sensors on their bodies to keep track of their daily activities.

4. *Text summarization How to make a summary* 必要な情報のまとめ方

Practice 5 **Summary of Topic 1 Recite it** Topic 1（前ページ）のまとめ 暗唱しよう

1. The giraffe's anatomy is unique, because it needs some special mechanisms to support its survival.
2. A giraffe has a lung capacity that is about eight times greater than that of the average human.
3. A giraffe's heart is the biggest of all land mammals.
4. Due to its high blood pressure, a giraffe has a special mechanism called a "wonder net."
5. A series of valves in a giraffe's jugular vein also regulate blood flow.
6. The giraffe's unique physical characteristics have inspired researchers and engineers.

Practice 6 **Read and summarize** 読んで内容を把握してサマリーを作成しよう 63

Giraffes are the tallest animals on Earth. Their legs alone are the size of an adult human. They can use their legs to run at speeds up to 55 km/h when avoiding **predators**《捕食動物》.

Despite its unusually long length, a giraffe's neck contains only seven bones. Surprisingly, that is the same number as those found in a human neck. However, the giraffe's **vertebrae**《脊椎》 are much larger than those of humans.

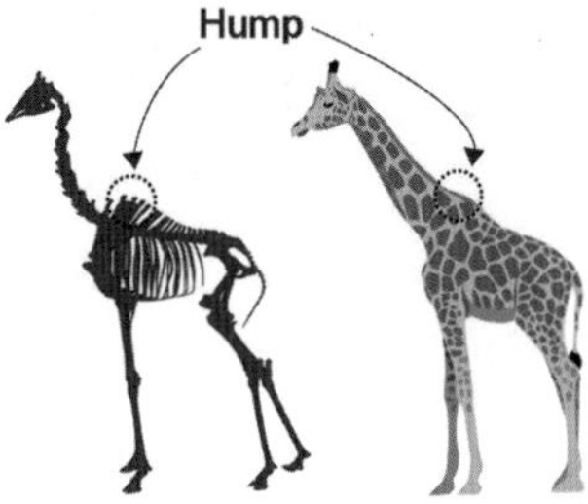

Giraffes have a small **hump**《こぶ》 on their backs as camels do. They also have a spotted skin pattern like leopards. In fact, a giraffe was once called a 'camel leopard,' because people believed that it was a hybrid of a camel and a leopard. This also explains the origin of the giraffe's scientific name, *Giraffa camelopardalis*.

Giraffes need only about 30 minutes of sleep per day. They can even sleep while standing. Since giraffes spend 16 to 20 hours per day eating leaves from tall trees and bushes, it's no wonder that they have so little time to sleep.

Giraffes are usually quiet animals. However, when they become alarmed, they can make various sounds, such as moos, roars, snorts, hisses, and grunts. Studies suggest that giraffes can vocalize at a frequency below the level of human hearing and perhaps use this sound for long-distance communication.

Complete the summary 適切な語を入れてサマリーを完成しよう

Giraffes are the ( ) animals on Earth. Giraffes have the same number of ( ) bones as humans. Giraffes have a small ( ) on their backs as camels do and need only about 30 minutes of ( ) per day. Giraffes are usually ( ) animals, but they can make various sounds when they become ( ).

Research **What are you interested in when reading this passage? Choose one and do research.**

5. Topic 2 The development of Shinkansen train cars 64

新幹線車両　開発エピソード

Practice 7 **We can learn many things from nature. An engineer was inspired by birds when designing new Shinkansen trains. What do you want to create by learning from nature?**

ヒトは自然から何を学ぶべきでしょうか？

Many Shinkansen trains have long-pointed noses now. These unique designs enable the trains to travel quietly at high speeds. However, this was not always the case.

Earlier models of the Shinkansen had short-rounded noses and noise problems. One source of noise was the pantograph, which is a device that connects the train to the overhead wires. Also, a loud **tunnel booming noise**《トンネル微気圧波の音》 occurred whenever the train left a tunnel.

Dr. Eiji Nakatsu, an engineer who worked on the train's redesign, was an avid bird-watcher. While trying to solve the train's noise problems, he was inspired by three birds: the **owl**《フクロウ》, the Adélie penguin, and the **kingfisher**《カワセミ》.

Dr. Nakatsu and his team reshaped the pantograph by studying the flight of owls. They mimicked the way of owls' primary feathers. The new design minimized **vortices**《渦》 and produced fewer vibrations and less noise. In addition, the pantograph's supporting shaft was redesigned for lower wind resistance, based on the smooth body shape of the Adélie penguin.

Dr. Nakatsu also got inspiration from a kingfisher diving into the water without splashing in order to solve the tunnel boom problem. His team discovered that the best shape for the train's nose was one that resembled the long, curved **beak**《くちばし》 of the kingfisher.

These newly designed trains debuted in 1997. They ran 10% faster, used 15% less electricity, and met environmental noise standards. This is a successful example of **biomimetics**《バイオミメティクス：生物模倣》, which is the concept of solving complex problems by imitating nature.

6. *Understanding learning from nature Key terms* 自然の学びに必要な用語

Practice 8 **Discuss the key terms on learning from nature: wonder net, the lotus effect, fish navigation, and nature observation.**

Wonder net

With a head so high above its **torso**《胴体》, the giraffe needs a powerful heart to pump blood through its long neck up to its brain. However, when the giraffe lowers its head to drink, what prevents a sudden rush of blood to the head? The answer lies in the wonder net. This special mechanism regulates blood flow to the giraffe's brain, together with a series of valves in its jugular vein. It protects the giraffe from being overwhelmed by sudden **surges**《一時的な急上昇》 in blood pressure as well.

The lotus effect

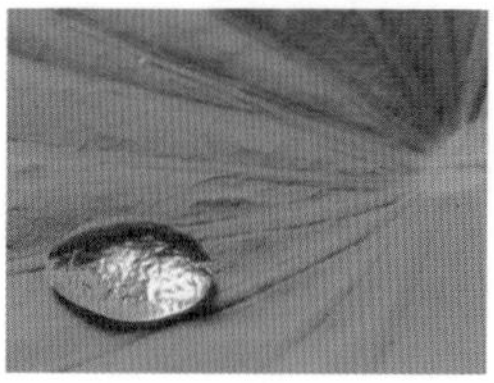

Lotus leaves《ハスの葉》 can stay clean naturally without the use of **detergent**《洗剤》 or energy. Called the 'lotus effect,' this self-cleaning mechanism arises from the fact that lotus leaves have special **surfaces**《表面》 which are extremely **water-repellent**《撥水性の》. This enables water droplets to roll off easily, thus carrying away dirt with them.

Fish navigation

Many fish can swim together closely in a group called a **school**《群れ》. They can even do this while avoiding **obstacles**《障害物》. After studying this behavior, engineers have found certain rules

that are useful for the development of traffic management systems. New **collision-free**《衝突しない》 technologies based on these findings lead to fewer accidents and less congestion on roadways.

Nature observation

The first step to learn something new is to simply observe something. This is especially true when it comes to living organisms and natural phenomenon. And the best part is you don't even have to be a scientist to make good observations. You only need curiosity, patience, and a keen eye for detail.

7. *Learning outcomes What have you learned?* 学んだことの整理

Self-assessment 自己評価をしよう

I can listen to and read **what nature learning is**.	0---30---50---70---100%
I can speak and write about **how nature learning works**.	0---30---50---70---100%
I can understand **the ideas and problems about nature learning**.	0---30---50---70---100%

Practice 9 A summary of learning: write a summary of what you have learned in this unit.

Key terms

Key sentences

Key facts

Your understanding

Your thoughts

Technology column 4: withdrawing water from the air 65

Discuss what you learned about it and what you want to know about it.

In the desert, water is not easy to access. Usually, it is obtained by digging wells or **desalinating**《脱塩する》 seawater. However, in the near future, we may be able to harvest water from the air.

A research team at UC Berkeley has developed a device that uses sunlight and dry desert air to harvest a cup of water. The key element of the device is 'a metal-organic framework (MOF),' a molecular terminal that is highly **porous**《多孔質の(穴が多い)》 and acts like a sponge to absorb water. MOF powder packed into a **plexiglass**《プレキシグラス(アクリル樹脂のガラス)》 top frame is **saturated**《飽和する》 during the humid cool night. During the day, the moisture warmed by the sun is released and **condenses**《凝縮する》 on the sides of the box **insulated**《断熱された》 with soil, forming water. By opening the box at night and closing it during the day, the temperature difference enables the **extraction**《抽出》 of water from the air. This device produces water from the air without the use of any energy other than sunlight.

MOF is expensive and **impractical**《実用的ではない》 because it uses **zirconium**《ジルコニウム》, according to the UC Berkeley and MIT research teams. Recently, however, an alternative, known as MOF-303, was invented. Since it uses aluminum instead of zirconium, MOF-303 can produce water at 1/53 of the cost of MOF.

The above technology has made it possible to produce water in deserts, but some people caution that it is just a theoretical approach.

Each person is estimated to consume approximately 150 liters per day, but MOF-based devices cannot produce so much water. If you need a glass of water, you can use them. It is not realistic to harvest enough water from the air. Besides, from a **hygienic**《衛生的な》 perspective, it is not possible to generate water that is directly drinkable.

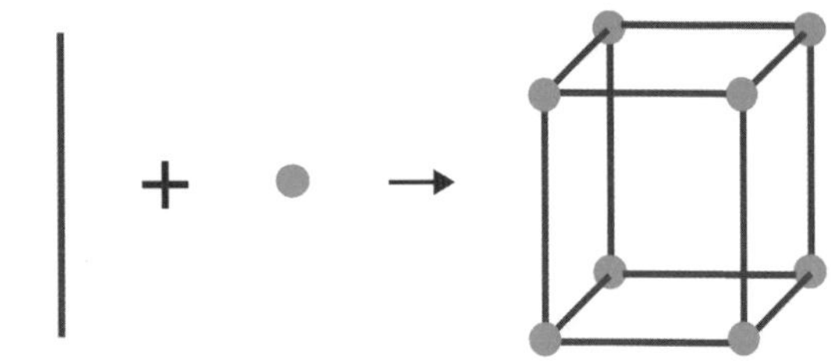

Paragraph writing about Technology column 4

What did you learn about this topic?

What do you want to know more about this topic?

Glossary

Unit 1	語句	意味
2. Introduction	solution	解決
	intervention	介入
3. Topic 1	take over	引き継ぐ
	birthrate	出生率
	aging	老齢
	compensate for	補う
	automatically operating machinery and equipment	自動で機械や道具を操作すること
	symbiotic relationship	共生関係
	on the contrary	他方
	medical care	医療
	predict	予測する
	outcome	結果
	supremacy	卓越
	distinguish	区別する
	speech recognition	発話認識
4. Text summarization		
Practice 6 Read and summarize	mathematician	数学者
	rational behavior	合理的行動
	manufacturing	製造業
5. Topic 2	surpass	越える
	strengthen itself	強くなる
	intelligence	知性
	the world of science fiction	SF の世界
6. Understanding key terms	potential	可能性
	adapt to	適応する
	blind-spot monitoring	死角チェック
	cross-trafic detector	交差交通検出
	autonomous vehicle	自律運転自動車
	inspired	触発された
	artificial neural network	人工神経
	endow	授ける

Unit 2	語句	意味
2. Introduction	vet	獣医
	three-dimensional	３次元の
	layering material	層状物質
	polymer filament	ポリマーフィラメント
	metal powder	金属粉
	manufacturing	製造業
	architecture	建築
	medicine	医療
	prototype	試作品
3. Topic 1	additive manufacturing	積層造形
	stack	積み重ねる
	solid	固体
	hollow	中空
	horizontally	水平に
	Fused Deposition Modeling (FDM)	熱溶解積層法
	Stereolithography (SLA)	ステレオリソグラフィー
	Digital Light Processing (DLP)	デジタル光造形
	Selective Laser Sintering (SLS)	選択的レーザー焼結
	Selective Laser Melting (SLM)	選択的レーザー溶融法
	Laminated Object Manufacturing (LOM)	薄膜積層法

	Electron Beam Melting (EBM)	電子ビーム溶解法
4. Text summarization		
Practice 6 Read and summarize	**prosthetics**	人工装具
	organ	臓器
	equipment	器具
	automobile	自動車
	remarkable	顕著な
	conventional means	従来の方法
	replacement organ	代わりの臓器
	organ donation	臓器提供
	bioprinting	バイオプリンティング
	cell tissue	細胞組織
	reduction	減少
	fuel efficiency	燃焼効率
	A-pillar	自動車の前窓の柱
5. Topic 2	**originate**	始まる
	patent	特許
	expire	期限が切れる
	function	機能
	performance	性能
	versatility	多用途性
	sinister	邪悪な
	nightmare	悪夢
6. Understanding key terms	**injection molding**	射出成形
	molten material	溶解金属
	die	金型
	polymer bead	ポリマービーズ
	rendering design	完成予想描画
	virtualization software	可視化ソフトウエア

Unit 3	語句	意味
2. Introduction	**power convention technology**	電力変換技術
	semiconductor device	半導体素子
3. Topic 1	**copper wire**	銅線
	direct current (DC)	直流
	alternating current (AC)	交流
	sinusoidal wave	正弦波
	waveform	波形
	rectifier diode	整流ダイオード
	rectification	整流
4. Text summarization		
Practice 6 Read and summarize	**household outlet**	家庭用コンセント
	transformer	変圧器
	capacitor	キャパシタ
	wireless power transfer	ワイヤレス電力伝送
5. Topic 2	**discipline**	分野
	advent	出現
	ubiquitous	どこにでもある
	the extent to which	する程度
	downsize	小型化する
	lightweight	軽量の
	iteration	反復
	photovoltaic power station	太陽光発電所
	superconductivity	超伝導
6. Understanding key terms	**ampere**	アンペア
	thyristor	半導体整流素子

Column 1	語句	意味
	descipline	分野
	civillization	文明
	civilize	文明化する
	confortable	快適な
	military fortification	軍事要塞
	patent	許可を取る
	specialization	専門性
	civil engineering	土木工学
	master-apprentice	徒弟制度
	systematize	体系化する
	institutution	研究機関
	transportation	輸送
	information and communication technology (ICT)	情報通信技術
	enrich	豊かにする

Unit 4	語句	意味
2. Introduction	climate change	気候変動
	global warming	地球温暖化
	sea level	海抜
	gas emissions	ガス排出
3. Topic 1	absorb	吸収する
	carbon dioxide	二酸化炭素
	atmosphere	大気
	fossil fuel	化石燃料
	consumption	消費
4. Text summarization		
Practice 6 Read and summarize	wooden	木製の
	resilient	耐震性
	brick	れんがの
	designated	指定された
5. Topic 2	chemical-free	化学物質を含まない
	building materials	建材
	well-being	幸福感
	occupants	居住者
	a rainwater buffer	雨水緩衝材
	purify	浄化する
	biodiversity	生物多様性
6. Understanding key terms	land surfaces	地表
	ice sheets	氷床
	over time	時の経過とともに
	precipitation	降水量
	trap	閉じ込める
	micro-organisms	微生物
	contraction	縮小形
	-friendly	～に優しい
	synonyms	同意語
	minimize	最小化する

Unit 5	語句	意味
2. Introduction	tide	潮流
	tidal current	潮流
	blood circulation	血流
	efficiency	性能
	wind turbine	風力タービン
3. Topic 1	convert	変換する
	blade	ブレード；刃
	relative to	関連する

	section	断面
	apply a force	力をかける
	perpendicular	垂直の
	lift	揚力
	drag	抗力
	airfoil	翼
	streamlined shape	流線型
	conservation of mass	質量保存の法則
	moment	モーメント
	aerodynamics	空気力学
	Bernoulli's principle	ベルヌーイの定理
	pressure difference	圧力差
	the angle of attack	迎え角
4. Text summarization		
Practice 6 Read and summarize	spill	こぼれる
	container	容器
	over time	時がたっても
	steady flow	定常流
	unsteady flow	非定常流
	variable	変数
	fixed point	定点
	laminar flow	層流
	turbulent flow	乱流
5. Topic 2	potential energy	位置エネルギー
	kinetic energy	運動エネルギー
	mass	質量保存の法則
	mechanical energy	力学的エネルギー
	harness	利用する
	high-performance	高性能
	Betz Limit	ベッツの法則
	physicist	物理学者
	power output	出力
	power generation	発電
	torque	トルク
6. Understanding key terms	buoyancy force	浮力
	exert	力を及ぼす
	gravitational field	重力場
	thrust	推力
	velocity	速度
	relative flow velocity	相対流速
	Computational Fluid Dynamics (CFD)	数値流体力学
	prediction	予測
	mathematical modeling	数理モデル
	numerical analysis	数値解析
	virtual flow laboratory	バーチャル・フロー・ラボ

Unit 6	語句	意味
2. Introduction	EV (electric vehicle)	電気自動車
	environmental problems	環境問題
	air pollution	大気汚染
	electrification	電化
	emission	排出
	exhaust gases	排気ガス
	reductions	削減
3. Topic 1	vehicles	車
	associated with	～と関連した
	large-capacity	大容量の

	onboard batteries	車載バッテリー
	recharged	再充電される
	multiple motors	複数のモーター
	plug-in	プラグ差し込み式の
	kinetic energy	運動エネルギー
	alternative	代替の
	rechargeable	再充電できる
	main componets	主要な構成機能
	accelerator pedal	アクセルペダル
	conver A into B	A を B に変える
4. Text summarization		
Practice 6 Read and summarize	**passenger cars**	乗用車
	welfare	福利
	output power balance	出力パワーバランス
	performance	性能
	electric harvesters	電動刈取り機
	burden	負荷
5. Topic 2	**compared with**	と比較して
	emit	排出する
	exhaust gases	排気ガス
	conserve	保存する
	extract	抽出物
	flexibility	柔軟
	utilized	有効利用される
	storage compartment	収納区画
	hood	フード
	maintenace costs	維持費
	conventional	従来の
	pedestrians	歩行者
6. Understanding key terms	**regenerative braking**	回生ブレーキ
	electric generator	発電機
	subsequently	続いて
	direct current (DC)	直流
	alternating current (AC)	交流
	are equipped with	装備している
	converters	変換器
	Power Control Units (PCUs)	出力調整装置
	motor-driven hybrid	モーター駆動のハイブリッド
	voltage	電圧

Coumn 2	**語句**	**意味**
	dependence	依存
	accelerate	加速させる
	flood	洪水
	mega-solar power plant	メガソーラー発電所
	alternative	大替の
	mountainous	山岳の
	incadndescent	白熱の
	incvention	発明
	dual-focused	二重の

Unit 7	**語句**	**意味**
2. Introduction	**pollute**	汚染した
	eruption	噴火
	landslide	地滑り
3. Topic 1	**mobility**	可動性
	manipulation	操作
	the United States Defense Research Project Agency (DARPA)	国防高等研究計画局

	competition	競争
	acceleromener	加速度計
	gauge	測定する
	debri	デブリ (がれき)
	gyroscope	ジャイロスコープ
	detect	見つける
4. Text summarization		
Practice 6 Read and summarize	disaster-laden	災害に打ちひしがれた
	endanger	危険に晒す
	decommissioning	廃炉にすること
	dismantle	解体する
	radiation protection	放射能防護
5. Topic 2	unpredictable	予測できない
	ground-convering	地面を動く能力
	a semi-outonomous	半自律的
	destination	目的地
	maneuver	操作する
	treacherous	不安定な
	autonomously	自律的に
6. Understanding key terms	property	特性
	piezoelectric	圧電性の
	stir	かき混ぜる
	strain	ピンと延ばす

Unit 8	語句	意味
2. Introduction	prefix	接頭辞
	simply speaking	簡単に言うと
	application	応用
	athletic equipment	スポーツ用品
3. Topic 1	physicist	物理学者
	nanoscale	ナノスケールの
	semiconductors	半導体
	deform	変形する
	atom	原子
	molecule	分子
	one ~ at a time	ひとつずつ
	nanometers	ナノメーター
	a strand of DNA	一本鎖の DNA（核酸）
	mass	質量
	gravitational force	重力
	nanosized particles	ナノサイズの粒子
4. Text summarization		
Practice 6 Read and summarize	doctorate	博士号
	theoretical physics	理論物理学
	quantum electrodynamics	電子電磁力学
	partons	パートン模型
	hypothetical	仮説の
	nucleus of the atom	原子の核
	quarks	クォーク
5. Topic 2	advancement	進歩
	nanofabrication	ナノ加工
	optical lithography	光リソグラフィ
	nanoimprint lithography	ナノインプリントリソグラフィ
	flexibility	柔軟性
	reliability	信頼性
	ongoing	進行中の
6. Understanding key terms	efficiency	効率
	energy consumption	エネルギー消費

	advocates	支持者
	graphene sheets	グラフィン：結合炭素原子シート
	cylindrical shape	円筒形
	electrical properties	電気特性
	biochemical	生物化学的
	organic	有機的
	quantum	量子
	microscope	顕微鏡

Unit 9	語句	意味
2. Introduction	generate	生成する
	generator	発電機
	emission	排出
3. Topic 1	electrification	電化
	feasible	実現可能な
	geothermal	地熱の
	hydroelectric	水力発電の
	exhaust has	排気ガス
	torque	トルク
	think otherwise	そうは考えない
	chemical reaction	化学反応
	combine with	化合する
	redox reaction	レドックス（酸化還元）反応
	Coredia iLint	コラディア・アイリント
	Buxtehude	ブクステフーデ
	Cuxhaven	ククスハーフェン
4. Text summarization		
Practice 6 Read and summarize	polymer electrolyte fuel cell (PEFC)	固体高分子形燃料電池
	low-temperature operation	低温運転
	power density	電力密度
	energy conversion efficiency	エネルギー交換効率
	cathode	カソード
	molecule	分子
	electrolyte membrane	電解質膜
	catalyst	触媒
5. Topic 2	steam reforming	水蒸気改質
	catalyst	触媒
	electrolysis	電気分解
	energy density	エネルギー密度
6. Understanding key terms	electrode	電極
	substantial	重要な
	traction	トラクション；牽引力

Column 3	語句	意味
	expertise	専門知識
	sophistication	精巧
	ajustment	調整
	unconsciously	無意識に
	optimize	最適化する
	integration	統合
	dilemma	ジレンマ

Unit 10	語句	意味
2. Introduction	tissue	組織
	amino acid	アミノ酸
	peptide bond	ペプチド結合
	polypeptide chain	ポリペプチド鎖
3. Topic 1	protein crystal	タンパク質結晶
	X-ray crystallography (XRC)	X線結晶構造解析
	irradiate	照射する

	convection	対流
	microgravity	微小重力
4. Text summarization		
Practice 6 Read and summarize	crystallization	結晶化
	microgravity	微小重力
5. Topic 2	astronaut	宇宙飛行士
	structural biology	構造生物学
	antibacterial drug	抗菌薬
	muscular dystrophy	筋ジストロフィー
	Alzheimer's disease	アルツハイマー病
6. Understanding key terms	organic molecule	有機分子
	organism	有機体
	nitrogen	窒素
	peptide band	ペプチド結合
	polypeptide chain	ポリペプチド鎖
	configuration	立体構造
	amino acid side chain	アミノ酸側鎖
	aerospace	宇宙空間
	core performance agency	中核的実施機関
	integrated operation	統合運用

Unit 11	語句	意味
2. Introduction	solar power	太陽光発電
	photovoltaics	太陽光発電
	hydroelectric power	水力発電
	geothermal power	地熱発電
	biomass	バイオマス
	greenhouse gas	温室効果ガス
	emit	排出する
	fossil fuel	化石燃料
3. Topic 1	global warming	地球温暖化
	climate change	気候変動
	convert	変換する
	thermal	熱の
	abundant	豊富な
	solar panel	太陽電池パネル
	photovoltaic (PV) panel	太陽光（PV）パネル
	photovoltaic effect	光起電力効果
	carbon footprint	カーボンフットプリント
4. Text summarization		
Practice 6 Read and summary	deforestation	森林伐採
	transportation fuel	輸送用燃料
	dependence	依存
	patronize	ひいきする
	extreme weather	異常気象
5. Topic 2	replenish	補充する
	decontaminate	除染する
	sustainability	持続可能性
6. Understanding key terms	electric generator	発電機
	motive power	原動力
	coils of insulated wire	絶縁導線コイル
	stationary cylinder	固定シリンダー
	electromagnetic	電磁気の
	localized	局所的な
	organic waste compound	有機廃棄物化合物
	steam turbine generator	蒸気タービン発電機
	ethanol	エタノール

	photosynthesis	光合成
	rooftop	屋上の
	hydro power	水力発電
	utility bill	光熱費
	tax incentive	税制上の優遇措置

Unit 12	語句	意味
2. Introduction	blood pressure	血圧
3. Topic 1	inhale	吸い込む
	mammal	哺乳類
	wonder net	奇驚網
	tissue	組織
	blood vessel	血管
	carotid artery	頸（けい）動脈
	jugular vein	頸静脈
4. Text summarization		
Practice 6 Read and summary	predator	捕食動物
	vertebrae	脊椎
	hump	こぶ
5. Topic 2	tunnel booming noise	トンネル微気圧波の音
	owl	フクロウ
	kingfisher	カワセミ
	vortex (複 vortices)	渦
	beak	くちばし
	biomimetics	バイオミメティクス；生物模倣
6. Understanding key terms	torso	胴体
	surge	一次的な急上昇
	lotus leaf	ハスの葉
	detergent	洗剤
	surface	表面
	water-repellent	撥水性の
	school	群れ
	obstacle	障害物
	collision-free	衝突しない

Column 4	語句	意味
	desalinate	脱塩する
	porous	多孔質の (穴が多い)
	plexiglass	プレキシグラス (アクリル樹脂のガラス)
	saturate	飽和する
	condense	凝縮する
	insulate	断熱する
	extraction	抽出
	impractical	実用的でない
	zirconium	ジルコニウム
	hygienic	衛生的な

CLIL in English–Technology and the Society [B-952]
CLIL で学ぶ工学と社会

1 刷　2023 年 2 月 7 日

著 者　笹島　茂　Shigeru Sasajima
高橋昌由　Masayuki Takahashi
上杉裕子　Yuko Uesugi
岡﨑久美子　Kumiko Okazaki
谷野圭亮　Keisuke Tanino
川上太知　Taichi Kawakami
勇地有理　Chiari Isami
ブライアン・ショー　Brian Shaw
アレクサンドラ・ザパルハ　Aleksandra Zaparucha

発行者　南雲　一範　Kazunori Nagumo
発行所　株式会社　南雲堂
〒162-0801　東京都新宿区山吹町 361
NAN’UN-DO CO.,Ltd.
361 Yamabuki-cho, Shinjuku-ku, Tokyo 162-0801, Japan
振替口座：00160-0-46863
TEL：03-3268-2311(代表)／FAX：03-3269-2486
編集者　加藤 敦

製 版　K-Atsu

装 丁　奥定泰之

コード　ISBN 978-4-523-17952-8　C0082

Printed in Japan

E-mail　nanundo@post.email.ne.jp
URL　https://www.nanun-do.co.jp/